Armstrong's River E

Tyne shipyards that supplied the world 1 ___ ___

Dick Keys and Ken Smith

Tyne Bridge Publishing

Acknowledgements

Unless otherwise stated, illustrations are ©Newcastle Libraries.

Some of the material in this book was included in *Down Elswick Slipways* by Dick Keys and Ken Smith, 1996 and *From Walker to the World* by Dick Keys and Ken Smith, 1997. Both books are now out of print. This book includes new information.

Thanks to Professor David Saunders of the University of Newcastle upon Tyne for his photographs of *Angara* and *Sviatogor*.

©Dick Keys and Ken Smith, 2010

Tyne Bridge Publishing
Newcastle Libraries
33 New Bridge Street West
Newcastle upon Tyne
NE1 8AX
www.tynebridgepublishing.co.uk
www.newcastle.gov.uk/libraries

ISBN: 978 1 85795 148 6

Published by
City of Newcastle upon Tyne
Newcastle Libraries
Tyne Bridge Publishing
2010

Printed by Elanders, North Tyneside

Front cover: Warships under construction at the Elswick Works, painted by Charles de Lacy, from the cover of the launch brochure for *Chao Ho*, 1911.

The central ship is the British battleship *Superb*. To the left of *Superb* the ship with the white hull is the Brazilian battleship *Minas Geraes*. These ships were lying together alongside the Elswick yard from September 1908 until February 1909. Also to be seen are ships on the stocks, a foy boat, paddle tugs to assist with launches (with their thrashing paddles, these were a great feature of the river scene up until the years immediately following the Second World War).

Back cover: the Japanese battleship *Hatsuse* is launched at Elswick on June 27, 1899.

Title page: Launch of battleship HMS *Victoria*, Elswick, 1887.

Some other books from Tyne Bridge Publishing on the Tyne's maritime history:

Emperor of Industry: Lord Armstrong of Cragside, Ken Smith
Turbinia: the Story of Charles Parsons and his Ocean Greyhound, Ken Smith
Lost Shipyards of the Tyne, Ron French and Ken Smith
Palmers of Jarrow, Jim Cuthbert and Ken Smith
Swan Hunter: the Pride and the Tears, Ian Rae and Ken Smith
Tales from the Tyne, Dick Keys and Ken Smith

Contents

HMS Victoria on her way down the Tyne, April, 6, 1888.

Lord Armstrong, above, aged just 20 in a portrait by Ramsey, and, right, as an elderly man in the doorway of his mansion, Cragside.

The Inventor

William George Armstrong was born on November 26, 1810, at No. 9 Pleasant Row, Shieldfield, Newcastle. The son of a prosperous corn merchant, he was destined to found one of the greatest armaments and shipbuilding businesses in Britain and his vast Elswick Works, in the West End of Newcastle, became the city's largest employer.

As a boy, William showed a keen interest in the practical world of making things and this was the spark which would lead him on to an intense interest in science, mechanics and engineering. It was a trail which would lead him even further to the invention of the hydraulic crane, to making his Northumberland mansion, Cragside, the first house in the world to be lit by hydro-electricity and to the invention of the Armstrong field gun.

However, his father, William Armstrong senior, had already mapped out his son's future. He set his sights on young William becoming a lawyer, and accordingly made arrangements with his old and trusted friend, the Newcastle solicitor Armorer Donkin, for William to train at Donkin's practice.

William duly underwent his training and

Pleasant Row, Shieldfield, Newcastle.

eventually became a partner in Donkin's solicitors' firm. But William junior continued to pursue his passion for mechanics and engineering in his free time. He often visited a factory owned by his friend, Henry Watson, in High Bridge, Newcastle, and saw telescopes, clocks and other items being made there.

In 1835, William became fascinated by the idea of water power and he drew up plans for a device using a rotary source of energy powered by water. The device was built in 1838 at Henry Watson's High Bridge works.

Armstrong continued to develop his water power ideas. Eventually he developed a system using a piston source of energy instead of a rotary one and decided that it might be suitable for driving a water powered (hydraulic) crane.

In 1845, Armstrong suggested a plan to put into practice the ideas he had developed for the crane. Supported by his legal partners, Donkin and G.W. Stable, he approached Newcastle Corporation and asked if he might adapt a crane on the Quayside to water power.

Armstrong would demonstrate that his hydraulic crane could unload ships faster and more cheaply than existing ones. The inventor and his friends, including Donkin, offered to carry out the modifications and trials of the crane at their own expense. The councillors agreed to the scheme. The adapted crane proved highly successful and three more hydraulic cranes were installed on the Quayside. These were built at Watson's High Bridge works.

The efficiency of William Armstrong's invention led him to consider setting up a business to manufacture the crane and other hydraulic equipment. He therefore resigned from the Newcastle legal practice.

Armorer Donkin was in favour of the business idea and, together with three other Newcastle men, George Cruddas, Richard Lambert and Addison Potter, backed the venture with money.

In 1847, the five business partners bought five and a half acres of land at Elswick, two miles west of the centre of Newcastle, and set up a factory there. The land was situated on the north bank of the Tyne between the river and a branch line of the Newcastle and Carlisle Railway. The riverside location was to prove an important asset for the future when the company would build warships and guns.

Armstrong threw himself with great energy and enthusiasm into developing the new business, which was named W.G.

Armstrong's hydraulic crane.

Armstrong and Company, working long hours to ensure the success of the venture. In founding the Elswick Works he was greatly helped by partner George Cruddas.

One of the first orders received for hydraulic cranes was from Liverpool Docks. Other early orders included cranes for the Edinburgh and Northern Railway and hydraulic machinery for dock gates at Grimsby. Soon, more docks and railways were turning to Elswick for their needs.

But William Armstrong was not content to remain merely a builder of hydraulic machinery. He eventually branched out into the fields of armament production and shipbuilding. Guns and cruisers joined the peaceful hydraulic crane on the list of products.

The guns came before the ships. In 1854-56, Armstrong invented a light, breech-loading field gun for the British Army, which was declared a great success. He surrendered the patents for the gun to the British government and received a knighthood as his reward. The honour was bestowed upon him in February, 1859, when he was presented to Queen Victoria.

However, it was the manufacture by Armstrong's company of naval guns, rather than land-based weapons, which led to the opening of a shipyard at the Elswick Works.

Armstrong had forged a pact with Charles Mitchell, who owned a shipbuilding yard at Low Walker in the East End of Newcastle. Under the agreement, Mitchell's yard was to build warships and Armstrong's Elswick Works would manufacture the guns for them.

The first vessel to result from this joint venture was the gunboat *Staunch*, delivered to the Royal Navy in 1868. She was 79ft long with a 25ft beam and carried a single 9-inch gun, mounted forward in line with her keel. More orders for gunboats followed. During the 1870s and early 1880s the Low Walker Yard completed 21 of these vessels, including 11 for China, three more for Britain, two for Holland and four for Australia.

The *Staunch* and its gun, intended for coastal defence, had been designed by George Rendel, a talented engineer who became a leading partner in Armstrong's company. The gunboat orders would lead on to greater developments.

Elswick Works around 1850.

The first Armstrong gun to be made at Elswick.

A Shipyard at Elswick

The completion of the Swing Bridge between Newcastle and Gateshead in 1876 began a new era in Tyneside's industrial history. Hitherto, an 18th century stone bridge of low arches had barred the passage of ships to and from the upper reaches of the Tyne where the Elswick Works were situated.

The demolition of this attractive but problematic structure and its replacement with the Swing Bridge, with its ability to open to let ships pass, meant the industrial development of the western half of Newcastle and Gateshead could accelerate. This was also greatly helped by dredging and the removal of other impediments to navigation carried out by the Tyne Improvement Commission.

The iron superstructure and machinery for the Swing Bridge were built by Armstrong's company. The remainder was the work of the Tyne Improvement Commission, which paid for the cost of the entire project. The scene was thus set for warships to be built at Elswick, 12 miles from the sea.

In July, 1876, the Italian warship *Europa* became the first

The Illustrated London News of July 29, 1876, shows Europa moving up river through the new Swing Bridge.

large vessel to pass through the Swing Bridge. She was on her way up river to the Elswick Works to take on board a 100-ton gun for the Italian navy.

The partnership arrangement between the Elswick Works and the Low Walker shipyard led to much closer ties. In November 1882, the firms of Armstrong and Mitchell agreed to merge. The new business took the name Sir W.G. Armstrong, Mitchell and Co. Ltd.

It was planned that most of the company's warship production would be transferred to a new yard at Elswick, with the Low Walker Yard concentrating mainly on merchant vessels. The two shipbuilding bases would constitute a kind of Tyne empire, with Sir William Armstrong presiding over the whole enterprise.

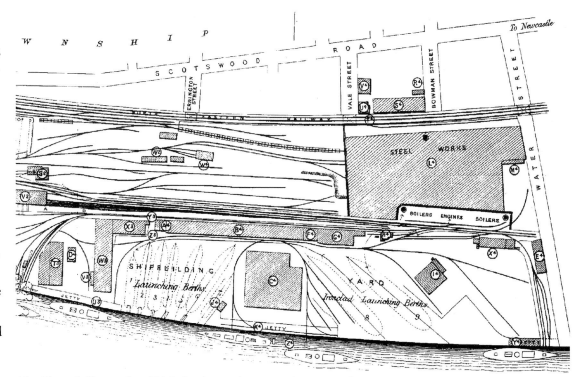

The Elswick Shipyard in 1886. On the stocks are HMS Renown (later Victoria), the Rattler and the Wasp. This drawing is from a brochure: 'A Visit to the Works of Sir W.G. Armstrong, Mitchell & Co. Ltd., Elswick, August 1886'.

The Elswick Shipyard opened for production in 1884, a little under two years after the merger, and soon it was a hive of activity. On Saturday, June 13, 1885, the Austro-Hungarian torpedo cruiser *Panther* became the first vessel to be launched there.

Thousands of spectators turned out to witness the ship's birth. From early afternoon the wives, children and friends of the workmen, as well as a substantial proportion of Elswick's population, thronged into the yard. Every vantage point was occupied and another crowd lined the opposite bank of the Tyne to gain a view of the warship entering the water.

Just after 3.30pm, the last impeding chocks were knocked clear. Lady Armstrong sent a bottle of champagne shattering against the *Panther's* bow and then the ship glided gracefully down the ways, entering the Tyne without mishap.

The Elswick Shipyard was situated to the south of Scotswood Road and almost immediately to the west of Water Street. Its site corresponds approximately to the present day Hampshire Court and eastern sections of Monarch Road and Amethyst Road, now part of Newcastle Business Park. There were nine building berths, laid out on either side of a steel plate workshop. The Elswick Works adjoined the site.

The opening of the yard heralded the start of an extraordinary chapter in Tyneside's history. Austria-Hungary was the first of many nations to place orders for warships, including a list that included Britain, Japan, China, Argentina, Chile, Brazil, Norway, Portugal, Spain, Italy, Turkey and Romania. In addition, the United States purchased two vessels originally intended for service with the Brazilian Navy.

Among the most prominent customers was the Imperial Japanese Navy, which took delivery of nine ships from the yard between 1893 and 1906. It was at the Battle of Tsushima in 1905 that Elswick vessels made their most dramatic impact upon the world stage. Tsushima was the most decisive engagement of the Russo-Japanese War. At this clash in the seas separating Japan and Korea, the Russian Baltic Fleet suffered a crushing defeat. The victorious Japanese ships were commanded by Admiral Heihachiro Togo.

Many of the Japanese fleet's guns were supplied by the Elswick Works and four of Togo's cruisers in the battle, the *Asama, Iwate, Idzumo* and *Tokiwa,* had been built at Elswick. Three cruisers launched at the company's Low Walker Yard, the *Idzumi, Naniwa* and *Takachiho*, also took part.

Low Walker's *Idzumi* had originally been constructed for the Chilean Navy in 1884 under the name *Esmeralda* and was the first of the company's so-called 'protected' cruisers. These ships were fast and relatively well-protected by the standards of the day, but from the late 1890s onwards the company began to launch more heavily armoured cruisers, such as the *Asama* and *Tokiwa*. By this time Elswick cruisers had become internationally renowned and for much of its life the yard specialised in this type of warship. They included a second *Esmeralda*, launched for Chile in 1896.

Two cruisers ordered by the Brazilian Navy were purchased by the United States. The first was the *New Orleans*, launched in 1895. Originally named *Amazona*s, the ship was handed over to the Americans shortly after completion in March 1898. The *New Orleans* took part in the blockade of Cuba and Puerto Rico during the Spanish-American War.

The second ship was the *Albany* (see launch card on page 42), which had been ordered by Brazil in 1897. She was bought by the US Navy in March 1898 when war between America and Spain became imminent. The ship was still on the stocks when purchased and was not launched until January the following year, by which time the Spanish American War had ended. During the First World War the *Albany* served as a convoy escort in the Atlantic.

Between 1885 and 1918 a total of 90 armed vessels were launched at the Elswick Yard, including battleships. One of the more unusual vessels was a royal yacht for the Sultan of Turkey, the *Erthogroul.* The list also included submarines.

But it was the torpedo cruiser *Panther* which began it all. Her keel was laid down on October 1, 1884. At the time, the yard was far from complete, so ship and yard took shape together. On her trials off Tynemouth the following year she achieved a speed of over 18 knots. It was a very creditable performance.

A view of Elswick Shipyard, probably taken in early 1885. The yard had opened for production the previous year and its first ship, the torpedo cruiser Panther, can be seen on the stocks. The Panther, built for the Austro-Hungarian Navy, was launched in June 1885. Three months later a sister ship, the Leopard, was also launched from the yard. This photograph was taken from King's Meadows island in the Tyne. The island was an obstacle to navigation and was soon to be dredged away by the Tyne Improvement Commission. The ship on the left is the Chilean ironclad Blanco Encalada, which was undergoing a refit. In 1891 she became one of the first vessels to be sunk by a torpedo.

As well as being the first Elswick-built warship, the *Panther* was also one of the first torpedo cruisers. This class of vessel was produced in reaction to a proliferation in the numbers of torpedo boats during the 1880s. Fast and armed with a deadly weapon, they caused considerable anxiety among naval authorities throughout the world, who had visions of their major ships being overwhelmed by swarms of these little craft. One of the solutions to the problem was to have a vessel better armed and with the speed to pursue and sink any offending torpedo boat.

The *Panther* was delivered to the Austro-Hungarian Navy complete and ready for sea, except for her armament and war-like stores. Paradoxically, while Armstrong Mitchell ranked amongst the world's foremost armament manufacturers, the contract to supply the guns for the first warship to be built at their new yard went to their arch-rival, Krupps of Essen. The guns were put aboard when she arrived at Pola in the Adriatic, then a base for her country's navy.

Although when first completed the ship was considered fast, it was not long before a new generation of torpedo boats eclipsed her capabilities. Unable to match their speed, the *Panther* soon became inadequate for the purpose for which she

First ship from the Elswick yard. The Austro-Hungarian torpedo cruiser Panther, launched in 1885.

had been designed. But despite this early obsolescence, she served the Austro-Hungarian navy for 35 years.

The end of the First World War also led to the end of Austro-Hungary as a country and to the dissolution of its navy. Under the terms of the Treaty of St Germaine the *Panther* was ceded to Britain, but she never returned to the country of her birth. Instead, in 1922 she was sold to shipbreakers in Messina, Italy.

Japanese cruiser Asama leaves the Tyne assisted by a paddle tug. Launched in 1898, she was damaged at the Battle of Tsushima in 1905 but managed to rejoin the fray. The Asama survived the Second World War, and was broken up in 1946-7.

The Japanese cruiser Iwate after her launch at Elswick on 30 March 1900. At the Battle of Tsushima she was hit 16 times but sustained only minor damage. During mopping-up operations on the second day of the battle Iwate played a leading role in sinking the Russian battleship Admiral Ushakoff. The Russian vessel fought bravely for three hours against the Iwate and another cruiser, the Yakumo. Hit below the waterline, the battleship eventually turned over and went down with the loss of 82 officers and men. Later in her career the Iwate became a training ship and survived until the Second World War. In July 1945 US carrier-borne aircraft located her near Kure, Japan, and she was attacked, sinking in shallow water.

Workers and Dignitaries

In 1897 the Armstrong Mitchell company underwent another transformation when it amalgamated with the Manchester-based armaments firm of Sir Joseph Whitworth and became known as Sir W.G. Armstrong, Whitworth and Co. Ltd. Armstrong had received a peerage ten years earlier, in 1887, when he was created 1st Baron Armstrong of Cragside.

By 1886 the Elswick Works was employing up to 12,000 people, and by 1906 this figure had reached 23,000 when working to full capacity. The works and shipyard dominated the economy of Newcastle's West End and there can have been few families in the terraced rows of the district who did not have at least one family member working for Armstrong's business. The company also opened a factory at nearby Scotswood which specialised in producing shot, shells and fuses.

Admiral Togo during his visit to Newcastle in 1911. Left to right, Admiral W.C. Dundas, Admiral Togo (seated), Sir Andrew Noble, Commander S. Saito, Lady Noble and Commander N. Taniguchi. This photograph was taken at Sir Andrew's home, Jesmond Dene House.

High-ranking naval officers and representatives of foreign governments came to the shipyard to witness launches and, along with their crews, to take delivery of vessels. Dignitaries also arrived to tour the works, not least of them the victorious Admiral Togo of Japan, who, in 1911, stayed as the guest of Sir Andrew Noble, then chairman of Armstrong Whitworth, at his home, Jesmond Dene House in Jesmond Dene Road, Newcastle. The admiral was accompanied by his A.D.C., Commander N. Taniguchi, and Commander S. Saito.

Togo, one of the few foreigners to hold Britain's Order of Merit, spent a full day at Elswick, arriving at the Water Street entrance of the works with his staff shortly after 10am. He was given a guided tour by three directors who first took him to the steelworks and ordnance department.

The quiet but charismatic admiral saw guns in various stage of manufacture and was also shown models of some of the ships built for the Imperial Japanese Navy. They included the *Naniwa*, which Togo had commanded, and the battleship *Hatsuse*.

After the models came the real vessels. The party were taken to the shipyard where they boarded HMS *Monarch*, a battleship in the process of being fitted out. The vessel had been launched from the yard in March of that year. The admiral and his staff then went on to inspect the cruiser HMS *Weymouth*, which had recently completed trials.

After lunch was served, the guests visited various workshops, where messages of welcome were displayed. In the forge, tools and castings had been arranged on the floor to form the words: 'Welcome to Admiral Togo, O.M.'. The admiral was said to have taken a deep interest in everything he was shown.

Next, the visitors were taken by motor cars to Scotswood where they saw 13.5-inch shells being made. They then toured Armstrong Whitworth's motor car production section. Togo and his entourage returned to Elswick for tea around 5pm.

During his three-day stay in Newcastle, the admiral was also received by the Lord Mayor and took a trip down the Tyne in a steam launch.

Among the many other VIPs to visit the shipyard and works was Winston Churchill, who arrived in October 1913 in

Workers at the Elswick shipyard in 1912.

his capacity as First Lord of the Admiralty. Churchill spent part of his visit aboard the Admiralty yacht *Enchantress*, which was moored in the river. Accompanied by Rear Admiral Moore and General Sir Ian Hamilton, he toured the yard, steelworks and ordnance factory.

The man destined to become Britain's Prime Minister during the Second World War inspected the battleship *Rio de Janeiro*, which had been ordered by the Brazilian Navy but which was later sold to Turkey, only to be seized by Britain on the outbreak of war in 1914 and renamed HMS *Agincourt*.

He went on to visit other Tyne yards, including the newly opened Walker Naval Yard in Newcastle's East End, which would eventually replace Elswick as Armstrong's warship building base on the river. A tour was also made of the St Peter's Works of Hawthorn Leslie and Co Ltd., which constructed some of the engines for Elswick ships.

But behind the much publicised official visits of dignitaries and the launching ceremonies lay the realities of shipbuilding life with its hard work, pressures and considerable dangers. The risk of accident was always present and lives could be lost.

For example, a fatal accident occurred during the building of the battleship *Hatsuse* in 1899-1901. Donald McMillan, of Frank Street, Benwell, Newcastle, was working on scaffolding erected around the ship's hull. It was a frosty day and this made the planking extremely slippery. A loose board had been left lying on top of the planks. It was a lethal combination and Donald McMillan tripped over the board, slipped and

Building berths at Low Walker shipyard. (From 'The Shipyards of Armstrong Whitworth', 1921.)

plummeted to his death some 30ft below.

Another tragedy occurred during the fitting out of the Chinese cruiser *Chih Yuan* in 1887. A caulker named Thomas Malloy was cutting a hole in the forward bulkhead of the stokehold. His workplace was dark, enclosed and badly ventilated. It only needed an infusion of coal gas to make it a death trap. That is what happened as the unfortunate Thomas Malloy carried out his task. He was found collapsed after being overcome by the fumes and died soon afterwards in the Newcastle Infirmary. An inquest was held at the Durham Ox

Inn. The jury returned a verdict of 'Death through coal gas poisoning'.

A very gruesome accident occurred in August 1897 shortly before the new Japanese battleship *Yashima* sailed from the Tyne. She had been brought down from Elswick to moorings off Jarrow Slake. Last-minute adjustments to her machinery were being made. One of the hydraulic ammunition hoists leading to the upper deck had been causing trouble and three fitters were requested to check it over. One of them remained below while his two workmates climbed to the upper deck to give the apparatus a trial run. When all was ready he shouted: 'Heave up!' The mechanism was set in motion. As the hoist came into view the horrified men above found themselves looking at their workmate's decapitated head.

Jarrow Slake was also the scene of another accident connected with an Elswick-built ship. In October 1889 the completed Italian cruiser *Piemonte* was moored there and not far away the Tyne wherry *Fanny*, carrying gunpowder and ammunition for the ship, also lay moored. Suddenly there was an explosion, followed by other blasts and *Fanny* erupted into flames. Shells were exploding. The little wherry's skipper, Edward Lowrie, jumped overboard and swam clear along with the skipper of another wherry which had been visiting.

Those whose reactions were slower were not so fortunate. One man was killed and two others badly burnt. Among the injured was an official from the Elswick Works and a 15-year-

The Frame Shop at one of the Armstrong yards, around 1920. (From 'The Shipyards of Armstrong Whitworth', 1921.)

old boy. Miraculously the wood-built *Fanny* remained afloat, an exploding menace to all in the vicinity. Eventually, an unnamed hero managed to scuttle her.

As soon as they heard the explosion the Italians aboard the *Piemonte* lost no time in sending a boat to give assistance to the vessel's men. The injured were taken off and given first aid by a doctor called from the floating quarantine hospital which was nearby. Two days after the *Fanny* incident, the newly-completed *Piemonte* left the Tyne for the Italian naval base at La Spezia.

The following year it was a boiler which caused trouble. While the cruiser *Pandora*, later to be known as the *Katoomba*, was fitting out at the yard in September 1890, 16 men received burns. It happened as the ship's boilers were undergoing their initial tests. Two had been lit, and to promote better circulation of water a few tubes had been removed. Suddenly, flames rushed out from the ashpit of one of the boilers, enveloping workmen nearby. Most of the burns were superficial and after treatment at the Newcastle Infirmary the victims were able to return home, except for one unfortunate man who was more seriously hurt.

The *Katoomba* was one of five warships built at Elswick especially for service on the Royal Navy's Australian Station. She served in Australian waters until 1905.

However, life at the yard was not all work. Sometimes there were sporting moments. In August 1890 the uncompleted torpedo gunboat *Plassy*, which was being built for the Royal Indian Marine, was used by the shipyard manager and some guests as a viewing platform for the Elswick Works Regatta.

The main event was a race from a point below the suspension bridge at Scotswood to a position abreast of the Elswick Works. The boats were manned by company workmen and the crews of the naval ships completing at the yard.

Five oared whalers belonging to the warships were used. In the preliminary round the workmen put up a very creditable

Lord Armstrong at the launch of the Pandora.

performance by beating the picked crews of the *Katoomba* and another Australian cruiser, the *Mildura*.

The combination crew of two other Australian ships, the torpedo gunboats *Boomerang* and *Karrakatta*, were the only warship men to escape defeat.

Chinese Sailors

Of the many warships built at the Elswick Yard, few could have aroused as much interest among the people of Newcastle as the Chinese cruisers *Chih Yuan* and *Ching Yuan*. The *Chih Yuan* was the first of the pair to be launched. The ceremony on September 19, 1886, was to Western onlookers an unusual affair. No women were allowed to stand on the launch platform and no brass band played the Chinese national anthem or a jaunty nautical air as she slid down the ways. Instead, cannons boomed in salute at the waterside.

Lord Sudeley, one of the dignitaries present, spoke about the ship's name when he addressed the reception following the launch. According to him, 'Chih Yuan' meant 'Go to far places and demolish all you come across'. His interpretation evoked a gale of laughter from some of the Western guests present.

But Mr Fung Lee, who replied on behalf of the Chinese Minister in London, who was unable to be present, administered a polite diplomatic rebuke by remarking that 'there were perhaps not many who understood Chinese'. How correct he was. He went on to give his own translation of the cruiser's name: 'There is no distance to which this cruiser

Tyne & Wear Archives & Museums

The launch party assemble on the platform for the launch of the Chinese cruiser Ching Yuan. As with the Chih Yuan, no women were allowed to stand on the launch platform.

cannot extend and no enemies she is not able to overcome.' This time there was no laughter, only applause.

Early in June 1887 the Chinese transport ship, *Too Nan*, entered the Tyne and berthed alongside the grain warehouse on Newcastle's Quayside. Aboard her was Admiral W.M. Lang and nearly 600 officers and men of the Imperial Chinese Navy. They had come to collect the two cruisers being built at Elswick and other warships nearing completion at Stettin in Prussia.

Newcastle had played host to seamen of many nationalities, but this sudden influx of Chinese sailors engendered more than the usual level of curiosity.

The Chinese cruiser Chih Yuan, launched at Elswick in 1886. She was sunk at the Battle of the Yalu during the Sino-Japanese War in 1894. The opposing ships at this engagement included the Elswick-built Japanese cruiser Yoshino.

Contemporary accounts describe the dress of the sailors: dark blue uniforms, light blue waist scarves and black turbans.

The officers wore close fitting Chinese hats and dark blue suits with black velvet facings and trimmings. Members of a rank or grade described as 'secretaries' were resplendent in silken robes of light blue and white. The sailors' every move seems to have been followed with great interest by the people of the city.

When Admiral Lang, accompanied by almost his entire force, attended a performance of a play at the Tyne Theatre and Opera House in Westgate Road they provided the other members of the audience with a talking point which may well have eclipsed the play. Nearly half of the stalls had been reserved for the men. The officers were seated in the dress circle, while Admiral Lang and Captains Kew Pow Chin and Tan Shi Chang occupied a private box.

All 580 of them arrived after the performance had started. They marched up from the Quayside in columns of four. As each officer entered the theatre he presented his card. More than 80 crimson-coloured cards bearing Chinese characters with English translations were handed to the door keepers. Evidently, the Chinese sailors became the centre of attention. To British people, the sight of naval men using fans seemed very strange, but several of the officers, either unaware of the effect they were making or indifferent to it, made use of their fans with all the ease of a society lady of the day.

The burial of two Chinese sailors in St John's Cemetery, Elswick, caused the *Newcastle Daily Journal* to comment: 'The idle curiosity which in Newcastle follows all the walks abroad of the wanderers from the Flowery Land was not allowed to lapse even in the instance where death intervened'.

The sailors were Lien Chin Yuen, aged 21, and Chin Shou-Fu, aged 30, both natives of Foo Chien. They died in the Newcastle Infirmary. At 4am on June 6, 1887, a contingent of 40 shipmates, under the command of Captain Yeh, arrived at the Infirmary which was situated approximately where the Centre for Life is today. Carefully they wrapped the bodies in white sheets, then placed them in the coffins. Before the lids were secured the dead men's clothes were neatly folded up and laid beside them.

The Chinese coffins were very substantial affairs. They were black, built of strong wood, lined with lead and thickly coated with varnish. It took quite a long time and much effort to manhandle these heavy coffins from the mortuary on to the waiting hearses. The proceedings were watched by another sick Chinese man from one of the windows of the Infirmary 'doubtless with an interest of the most painful and mournful character'.

The cortège made its way up Westmorland Road. The hearses and silent column of sailors then climbed Rye Hill and turned into Elswick Road. When the cemetery gates were reached an unexpected reception awaited them. About 200 curious onlookers had got out of their beds at that early hour to witness the interment. They crowded closely around, determined not to miss a single aspect of the ceremony.

The graves had been dug close to those occupied by two Chinese sailors who had died of consumption aboard the transport ship *Hai Shin*, while she lay at the Elswick Works in May 1881.

After the coffins had been lowered into the graves the contingent of sailors, with their officers to the fore, knelt down in front of each grave in turn and silently bowed their heads to the earth five or six times. They then covered the coffins with soil and finished the funeral ceremony by igniting a heap of joss paper over each mound.

The nurses at the Infirmary paid their respects by sending a pair of wreaths, and two young sisters, the Misses Tailford, laid bouquets of flowers on the graves.

Six days later, again at 4am, another sailor, Chen Kin Qua, was laid to rest near his old comrades. Another large crowd had gathered and a police guard was mounted at the graveside. It was reported that on board the *Too Nan* nine other seamen were suffering from 'a malady peculiar to the Chinese'.

The gravestones of the three sailors still survive in St John's Cemetery, but they have been toppled over and now face downwards. Two Chinese headstones nearby, still in place, are those of the men from the transport ship *Hai Shin*.

An inscription fronting the headstones of the three men buried in 1887 reads: 'The tombstones of these three and two neighbouring graves were erected by the officers and crew of the Chinese cruisers *Chih Yuan* and *Ching Yuan*. To provide for these graves and the monument behind being kept in order a sum has been invested in the name of Mr Thos. Halliday who will apply the annual interest to that purpose.'

The *Too Nan* left the Tyne on June 20, 1887, with 291 of the sailors on board. They were on their way to Stettin to take delivery of two other cruisers. In August, it was the turn of the *Chih Yuan* and *Ching Yuan* to depart the river. They steamed southwards to Spithead to rendezvous with the Stettin ships and a torpedo boat which had been built at Poplar in London.

At about this point, the ships began to be noticed as well as their colourful crews. Their fighting potential came as a shock to some observers. Commenting on the Elswick vessels a correspondent of the *Army and Navy Gazette* wrote: '…it is humiliating but nevertheless an actual fact that the two cruisers of the Chinese squadron are superior in certain novelties of construction to any of our own vessels. In point of speed they

Dick Keys

The headstones of the three Chinese sailors who were buried in St John's Cemetery, Elswick, in 1887, photographed before they were toppled.

cannot be touched by our swiftest cruisers…'

Within a few days all the newly-built ships had assembled at Spithead and before August was out they weighed anchor and sailed to China via Suez.

There is evidence indicating that the Chinese sailors established friendships with Tyneside families and were, in at least one instance, entertained in their homes. One girl is reported to have married a sailor and to have gone out to China with her husband. Sadly, the marriage did not survive the cultural clash of the time. She and her child were believed to have been repatriated to Britain with the aid of Christian missionaries.

The *Chih Yuan* and *Ching Yuan* served the Imperial Chinese Navy for less than ten years. Both were lost during the Sino-Japanese War of 1894-95.

The *Ching Yuan* was sunk by shells fired from a fort at the Battle of Wei-Hai-Wei in February 1895. The ship and other surviving elements of the Chinese fleet, under the command of Admiral Ting, had been blockaded by Japanese warships in what was considered to be a fairly safe anchorage between the mainland port of Wei-Hai-Wei and the island of Leu-Kang.

On February 2, 1895, the Japanese Army took Wei-Hai-Wei. One by one the mainland forts fell to the Japanese and as they did so their guns were turned on the hapless Chinese ships. Simultaneously, the Japanese ships began a systematic bombardment which also served as a cover for a determined force of sailors who made a landing on Leu-Kung island to attack the gun batteries there. The once safe anchorage had become a death trap. The Japanese grip was so tight that when 14 Chinese torpedo boats made a spirited attempt to escape, all but two were sunk.

A flotilla of Japanese torpedo boats picked their way through the mined eastern entrance of the anchorage on the night of February 4-5. It was bitterly cold at the time, so cold that a lieutenant and two seamen froze to death at their posts aboard one of the torpedo boats. But the flotilla persevered and created havoc amongst the Chinese. The *Ching Yuan* was hit by

The Japanese cruiser Yoshino whose guns helped to sink the Chih Yuan.

a torpedo fired from the Japanese torpedo boat *T-11*. Although badly damaged, she remained afloat.

However, the fight was not all one-sided. Of the ten attacking torpedo boats only one got out of the anchorage without being damaged.

Three days after the torpedo boat raid the last but one of the Chinese forts was stormed. Early on February 9 the *Ching Yuan* received at least one direct hit, fired from the captured Fort Luchiaotsoi, which penetrated her deck and caused fatal damage to her hull. She went down in 30 minutes. Sixty of her crew lost their lives.

Hemmed in on all sides, Admiral Ting's position had become untenable, but he fought on with his remaining ships until the 12th, when he sent a gunboat under a flag of truce to the Japanese, who were under the command of Admiral Ito, offering surrender if the lives of his men were spared. The Japanese agreed to these terms, but Admiral Ting felt the humiliation of defeat so intensely that he committed suicide.

After the admiral's death the Chinese fleet came under the command of a Briton, Admiral McClure, a former merchant shipmaster, who carried out his late commander's wishes and surrendered. From all accounts the Japanese admiral remained true to his word. The captured sailors were treated well and soon released. Admiral Ting's remains and those of his subordinates who had died in the battle were sent, under a salute of guns, to Chefoo.

The crew of the *Ching Yuan* had fought bravely and with considerable tenacity but the Chinese Emperor was evidently unimpressed. For the 'crime' of surrendering, the men who defended Wei-Hai-Wei were sentenced to death. This probably included the surviving sailors. The governor of Shangtung was authorised to behead them without following the usual procedure of first reporting to the throne.

The other Elswick cruiser, the *Chih Yuan*, met her end at the Battle of the Yalu in September 1894 during a clash with a Japanese force which included the Elswick-built cruiser *Yoshino*.

The *Chih Yuan* tried to ram the *Yoshino*, but failed to hit her faster opponent. The Chinese cruiser was then sunk by gunfire. It was ironic that the fortunes of war had pitted one Elswick ship against another.

Last Chinese cruiser: the launch of the Chinese training cruiser Chao Ho, October 23 1911. This ship was probably the last to be launched for Imperial China before the country was engulfed by revolution. The launch card for Chao Ho is reproduced on page 37.

Battleship Victoria

HMS *Victoria* was the first battleship to be built at Elswick and at the time of her completion the heaviest and most expensive vessel ever constructed on the Tyne. She cost £724,855, a colossal sum by the standards of the 1880s.

Victoria's keel was laid on June 13, 1885, the same day as Elswick's first ship, the *Panther*, was launched. Guests who had assembled to see the *Panther* go down the ways were invited to witness Sir William Armstrong strike the first rivet into the structure of the new battleship. She was then known as the *Renown*, but only three weeks before her launch this was changed to *Victoria* in honour of Queen Victoria's Golden Jubilee Year, 1887.

The *Victoria*'s launch day, Saturday, April 9, 1887, acquired all the features of a public holiday. Many local businesses were closed. From early morning, spectators began arriving at every available vantage point on both sides of the Tyne. About 3,500 tickets were issued for visitors to the shipyard.

As Sir William had ceremoniously driven the first rivet into

Sir William Armstrong (in the top hat, centre back) surrounded by workers and spectators at the keel-laying ceremony of battleship HMS Victoria in 1885.

the ship, he was also on hand to strike home the last before the launch. By 3.30pm this task had been completed and the remaining chocks were knocked clear. Then, Mrs Forwood, wife of the Parliamentary Secretary to the Admiralty, pulled the handle of an apparatus which heaved a bottle of champagne against the *Victoria's* bow. Right on cue, the great ship began to move, the band of the 3rd Volunteer Battalion of the Northumberland Fusiliers struck up *Rule Britannia* and a mighty cheer went up from the thousands of onlookers.

As she entered the Tyne a huge wave was sent rolling across the river. It caught some of the less agile spectators standing on the opposite bank and gave them a thorough soaking.

After her launch the *Victoria* spent almost a year fitting out at Elswick. Her presence created an enormous amount of interest throughout Tyneside. In an unprecedented gesture, Armstrong Mitchell's allowed her to be inspected by the public on Easter Monday 1888. A substantial charge of one shilling for morning visitors and two shillings for those who came in the afternoon did not prevent a big turnout of people eager to look over the largest ship most them had ever seen.

An impressive view of HMS Victoria on the stocks at Elswick in 1887. Her propellers are waiting for more blades to be fitted.

A

Left: The launch of HMS Victoria on Saturday April 9, 1887. A huge wave was sent rolling across the Tyne, soaking some of the spectators on the Gateshead bank. Above: The Swing Bridge, Armstrong's gateway to the sea, opens to allow the ill-fated battleship HMS Victoria to pass through on April 6, 1888. Crowds on the quaysides and the High Level Bridge gathered to watch. Note the dense black smoke.

At 10am on April 6, 1888, the *Victoria* left her moorings at Elswick to begin the journey down river to the sea. The spectacle attracted huge crowds. But for some who managed to get what should have been a good viewing position on the High Level Bridge there was a disappointment in store. As the huge ship drew near, the *Daring*, one of the leading tugs, began emitting voluminous clouds of dense black smoke. Added to this was a similar emission from the *Victoria*'s own two squat funnels. The battleship was completely enshrouded in smoke.

Even in an era not exactly characterised by its environmental concern, the incident brought unfavourable comment in the annual report of the Tyne Improvement Commissioners. It was suggested that an example should be made of the *Daring*. As for the *Victoria*, her smoke problem was so bad she had to have her funnels lengthened at an early stage in her career. Prior to that, life on her upper deck in anything but a beam wind must have been extremely uncomfortable.

The passage down river to the sea was accomplished in two stages. The first ended at the grain warehouse on Newcastle Quayside, where she moored after being under way for only a couple of hours. She had negotiated the narrow south channel of the Swing Bridge without incident. The fact that a vessel with a breadth of 70ft and a draft of 26ft 9ins could safely navigate the Tyne above the Swing Bridge was an indication of how successful the Tyne Improvement Commission's dredging work of recent years had been. Only 25 years before it had been possible to wade across the river at low water at the place where the High Level Bridge stands.

The *Victoria* got under way again the following morning, also at 10am. Soon after, she ran aground at Bill Quay.

However, it was not long before the rising tide floated her off. As she passed the various shipyards the workmen were given time off to watch her go by. At North Shields, boys of the training ship *Wellesley* manned the yards. It was here that HMS *Valorous* joined her. The *Valorous* was the last paddle frigate to be built for the Royal Navy. She was on hand to escort the *Victoria* to Chatham. After being swung for compass adjustment off Cullercoats and after a few preliminary engine trials, the *Victoria* departed for the southern naval base.

In 1890 the vessel became the flagship of the Commander in Chief of the Mediterranean Fleet, Vice Admiral Sir George Tryon. Fate was to bring disaster to both man and ship during fleet manoeuvres. In June 1893 the *Victoria* was leading one of two columns of ships, steaming along in parallel lines off Tripoli in Lebanon (not to be confused with the Tripoli in Libya). Admiral Tryon gave the order for the columns to reverse course by turning inwards towards one another. The order was obeyed.

But the parallel lines of ships were not far enough apart to avoid calamity. Turning towards the *Victoria* and leading the other column was the battleship *Camperdown*. She struck the Elswick-built vessel a mortal blow on the starboard bow. Water rushed in and just over ten minutes later the *Victoria* capsized. She then slid beneath the waves, taking with her 358 officers and men, including the admiral.

A court martial in Malta later that summer found the loss of the *Victoria* was due to an order given by Vice Admiral Tryon. The ship's captain, Captain Maurice Bourke, was honourably acquitted of any blame. However, the court expressed its regret that Rear Admiral Hastings Markham, who was aboard the *Camperdown*, had not carried out his first intention of notifying the flagship that he doubted the possibility of completing the manoeuvre successfully.

Among the *Victoria's* survivors was the then Lieutenant Commander John Jellicoe, who was to become Commander in Chief of the Grand Fleet at the Battle of Jutland during the First World War.

The news of the loss of the *Victoria* was read with shock on Tyneside, not least by the craftsmen of Elswick. There was a slight fear that their workmanship might have been in some way at fault, but reassurance on this point was soon forthcoming. The details are contained in an account by a correspondent of the *Globe* who interviewed the now Lord Armstrong at Cragside soon after the disaster.

The correspondent wrote: 'While we sat talking, a servant came into the spacious living room bringing a letter. Lord Armstrong reads it, and, a slight smile of gratification passing over his venerable face, hands it to me. It is from Mr. W.H. White, the Director of Naval Construction, and bore testimony to the fidelity and care which, down to the smallest details, the *Victoria* was built at Elswick.'

HMS Victoria test fires her guns.

Any sentiment or concern which the directors of Armstrong Mitchell had over the loss of the *Victoria* was put aside when it came to be measured in terms of hard cash. Money was, as ever, the bottom line. At a board meeting on July 12, 1893, the idea of contributing to the HMS *Victoria* Relief Fund was rejected.

In 2004, 111 years after her sinking, the wreck of the *Victoria* was discovered by divers off Tripoli, over 350ft below the surface. Remarkably, the vessel was standing in a vertical position, with a large section of her hull embedded in the seabed.

Warships for Japan

Three Japanese warships built at Elswick were sunk on the same day in 1904 during the Russo-Japanese War. The loss of these vessels marked one of the worst moments for Japan in the conflict at sea.

The first of the trio to be launched was the cruiser *Yoshino*. Named after a mountain noted for its cherry blossom, she slid down the ways on December 12, 1892. The launch ceremony was performed by the wife of Philip Watts, the ship's designer. At the completion of steaming trials in July, 1893, the *Yoshino* was heralded as 'the fastest cruiser in the world'. The results of these trials were undoubtedly impressive. Running against the tide she made over 22 knots and with the tide in her favour 23. A Japanese crew was sent to Tyneside to man the *Yoshino* for the run home and on September 30, 1893, she was officially handed over. A couple of days before the cruiser's departure she was lying off Jarrow Slake when news arrived that 2nd cook, Suyckichi Ouchi, had died in Newcastle Infirmary. He had been involved in an accident at Elswick and developed pleurisy as a result. A funeral party from the ship travelled up the Tyne in their own steam launch to Elswick. A cortège was formed, the officers riding in cabs with the seamen following in the procession on foot. A crowd of several hundred onlookers had assembled at St John's Cemetery and scenes reminiscent of the burial of the Chinese sailors six years previously were re-enacted.

The body of Suyckichi Ouchi was buried in a coffin which contained a new set of clothes and a pair of boots. A wooden monument with an inscription in Japanese was erected. After a wreath in a glass case had been placed over the grave, the sailor's last resting place was sprinkled with water. Then the officers, followed by the men, stepped one by one to the foot of the grave and bowed.

The second of the three ships sunk in 1904 to be launched, was the *Yashima*. She was the first battleship built for the Imperial Japanese Navy at Elswick. Her keel was laid down on December 6, 1894, and she took 20 months to complete. Bearing the ancient poetic name of Japan, the *Yashima* was one of the largest and most formidable warships of her day. The ship's main armament included 20 three-pounder guns. There were five torpedo tubes. Her armoured belt was 18ins thick over the machinery spaces.

The launch of the *Yashima* was scheduled for 2.30pm on February 28, 1896, but when the time arrived the tide was not high enough. A strong westerly wind blowing down the Tyne was blamed for keeping the water back. It took another 30 minutes before the tide reached its predicted height. When it did, Madame Kato, wife of the Japanese Minister in London, released a bottle of champagne which smashed against the ship's bow. As it did so a flock of pigeons was released and after a moment the *Yashima* slid gracefully into the Tyne.

Following the ceremony, lunch was provided in the dining room of the Ordnance Works for a number of the most distinguished guests. Lord Armstrong, Earl and Lady Percy and Captain Yendo, the Japanese Naval Attache, were among those present. Sir Andrew Noble proposed a toast: 'To the designer of the *Yashima* – Mr Philip Watts.'

On May 14, 1897, shortly before her completion, the battleship was moored at Newcastle Quayside and thrown open to the public for viewing. Proceeds went to the New Infirmary Fund.

The third vessel was the battleship *Hatsuse*, launched on June 27, 1899. At that date she was the largest warship ever to come from the Tyne's slipways. On the same day, another record-breaking vessel was launched by Armstrong Whitworth, the merchant ship *Atlantian*. Built at the company's Low Walker Yard, she was the river's largest merchant vessel at that date. A contemporary account describes her as 'a peaceful argosy capable of transporting 11,500 tons'.

Such a description could hardly be applied to the *Hatsuse*, which, like the *Yashima*, carried four 12-inch guns. It was 5.30pm when the last chocks were knocked from beneath the *Hatsuse*. Her launching weight was 8,500 tons.

The spectacle of such a large ship entering the water naturally attracted many sightseers. From Newcastle Quayside came the Tyne General Ferry Company's steamer *Syren*,

The Japanese battleship Yashima off Newcastle Quayside, where the vessel was moored for public viewing. She hit at least one mine at Port Arthur in 1904, but remained afloat for several hours before sinking. This enabled most of her crew to be rescued.

crowded from stem to stern. Madame Arakawa, wife of the Japanese Consul General in London, performed the launching ceremony. She was watched by the Japanese Charge d'Affaires and representatives of the navies of the United States, Norway, Portugal, Chile and of course Japan. All these nations had ships in various stages of construction at Elswick.

The completion of the *Hatsuse* in January 1901 coincided with the death of Queen Victoria. One of the new battleship's first duties after leaving the Tyne was to steam to Spithead to join the warships of many nations lining the route from East Cowes to Portsmouth taken by the Royal Yacht *Alberta* as she bore the Queen's body from the Isle of Wight to the mainland. When the maritime cortège steamed by, the crews of the ships stood to attention on deck with heads bowed. Ensigns were dipped as a further mark of respect.

The Russo-Japanese War opened on the night of February 8, 1904, with an attack by Japanese destroyers against ships of the Russian Pacific Fleet lying at anchor off Port Arthur. The *Hatsuse* became flagship of Rear Admiral Nashiba, who was in command of the warships blockading the Russian-controlled port in north-eastern China. Among the vessels also taking part in the blockade were the *Yashima* and the *Yoshino*. On February 9, when the first shots were exchanged with the shore batteries, a shell exploded in the admiral's cabin, killing or wounding 16 men. It was a bad start, but worse was to come.

In April the Japanese sank the battleship *Petropavlovsk*. Among those killed was the brilliant Russian officer Admiral Makarov, who was aboard her. The sinking had been achieved by sowing mines at the entrance to Port Arthur. It was a lesson not lost on the Russians.

Captain Ivanoff, commander of the minelayer *Amur*, spotted a weakness in the operations of the blockading Japanese ships – they never varied their patrol lines. This predictability was to prove disastrous. On May 14 the *Amur* slipped out of harbour, evading the enemy, and laid mines across the patrol lines. The following morning along came the patrolling *Hatsuse, Yashima* and *Shikishima*.

The *Hatsuse* was the first to hit one of the mines. The explosion which followed wrecked her steering gear and she became unmanageable. A towline from another vessel was put aboard, but soon afterwards she struck a second mine. A series of explosions followed. Within a few minutes the *Hatsuse* sank, taking more than 500 officers and men with her.

Next it was the *Yashima's* turn. It was thought she might have struck two mines. Whatever the number, she was holed badly. For a while her watertight bulkheads stayed intact and she remained afloat. A determined effort was made to tow the *Yashima* to safety but failed. After several hours she capsized. Fortunately, her crew had ample time to abandon ship and loss of life was small.

On the same day the cruiser *Yoshino* was manoeuvring in dense fog to the south of the Liao-Tung Peninsula on which Port Arthur is situated. Suddenly the Japanese armoured cruiser *Kasuga* loomed out of the murk and struck the *Yoshino* a fatal blow. A large hole was torn in her port quarter and she began to sink rapidly by the stern. This time, loss of life was heavy – numbers reported vary between 318 and 329 officers and men.

But the Japanese were to eventually win their war with Russia. At the Battle of Tsushima on May 27-28, 1905, Admiral Togo's ships inflicted total defeat upon the Russian Baltic Fleet commanded by Admiral Zinovi Rojestvensky. On the Russian side, 4,830 men were killed and eight battleships, four cruisers and five destroyers sunk. Nearly all their other ships were captured, wrecked or interned in neutral ports. Only three vessels managed to escape to the safety of Vladivostock. In contrast, the Japanese lost 117 men and only three torpedo boats. Togo's victory had been overwhelming.

In April 1906, Japanese sailors arrived on Tyneside to take delivery of the battleship *Kashima*, which had been launched at Elswick the previous year. The *Kashima* was the last warship to be built at the yard for the Imperial Japanese Navy. It was the

Three cheers! Hats are raised as the Japanese battleship Hatsuse glides down the ways on 27 June 1899.

end of an era, for it was no longer necessary for Japan to have such vessels built abroad. The Land of the Rising Sun was now able to construct its own warships.

More than 100 men of the *Kashima* and a group of officers watched a football match at St James's Park between Newcastle and Stoke during their visit to the city. The crew had spent the afternoon of Tuesday April 24, 1906, looking around the city centre.

When they arrived at the football ground they found welcoming messages displayed in Japanese writing. The men had tea with club directors and received a cheer from the crowd as they took their places in the stand. Many of the sailors had fought at the Battle of Tsushima and were regarded as heroes.

The men clearly enjoyed watching the match, and they generously applauded good play. Newcastle scored a resounding 5-0 victory in front of a crowd of 12,000.

The *Kashima* had been launched on a bright, sunny day, March 22, 1905, by Madame Arakawa, wife of the Japanese Consul General in London. Madame Arakawa was, by this time, a well known lady at Elswick. She had also launched the cruisers *Asama* and *Iwate* and the battleship *Hatsuse*.

The *Newcastle Daily Journal* reported that the ship 'was much admired as she lay on the stocks, gaily decorated with Japanese flags, evergreens etc. Suspended from her bow was a large collapsible cage covered in red and white striped material and containing a number of pigeons, which in accordance with national custom were released, together with a quantity of confetti, as the vessel glided into the water amid enthusiastic cheering from the crowds'.

The launch of the Kashima. The lady with the bouquet (third from the left on the platform) is Madame Arakawa, wife of the Japanese Consul General in London, who performed the ceremony. On the extreme left of the platform is Lady Noble, wife of the company chairman Sir Andrew Noble.

LAUNCH OF THE
· CHINESE ·
TRAINING-CRUISER
"CHAO HO"
From the Elswick
Shipyard
Newcastle·on·Tyne.
by Miss AMY LEW
OCTOBER 23rd 1911

Launch cards

Launch cards were issued to official guests at launching ceremonies. They were colourful and informative souvenirs with an artist's impression of the ship, the flag of her country, and the vessel's particulars. The ones shown in this section are from a collection of the Armstrong Whitworth cards in Newcastle City Library.

Chao Ho (pictured on page 25) was probably the last ship built on the Tyne for Imperial China. The ship was launched by Miss Amy Lew, daughter of 'His Excellency Yuk Lin Lew, Envoy Extraordinary and Minister Plenipotentiary to the Court of St James'. Unusually, the Chao Ho entered the water with machinery and boilers on board, funnels fitted and other work in an advanced stage. After the ceremony tea was served in the mould loft to representatives of the Chinese, Brazilian, Chilean, Spanish, Russian and Japanese navies, as well as civic guests.

CHAO HO

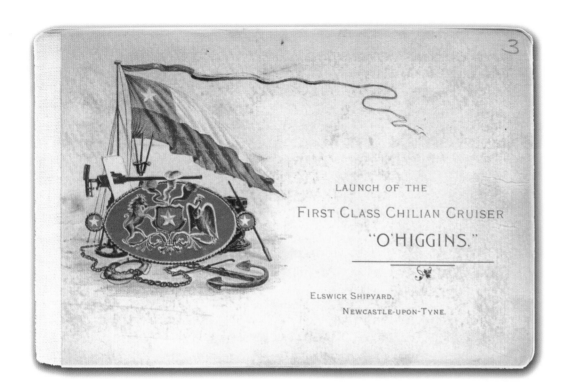

LAUNCH OF THE

FIRST CLASS CHILIAN CRUISER

"O'HIGGINS."

ELSWICK SHIPYARD,
NEWCASTLE-UPON-TYNE.

The Chilean armoured cruiser *O'Higgins*, built by Sir W.G. Armstrong, Whitworth & Co. Ltd., was launched from the Elswick Shipyard on May 17, 1897 by Doña Mercedes Valdes de Barros Luco.

Principal dimensions
Length: 412ft
Breadth 62ft 9ins
Draft, mean 22ft
Displacement in tons 8,500

Armament
4 8-in quick firing guns
10 6-in quick firing guns
4 4-7-in quick firing guns
10 12-pdr quick firing guns
10 6-pdr quick firing guns
4 machine guns
3 torpedo tubes
Barbettes, 6 ins thickness
Conning tower, 9 ins in thickness

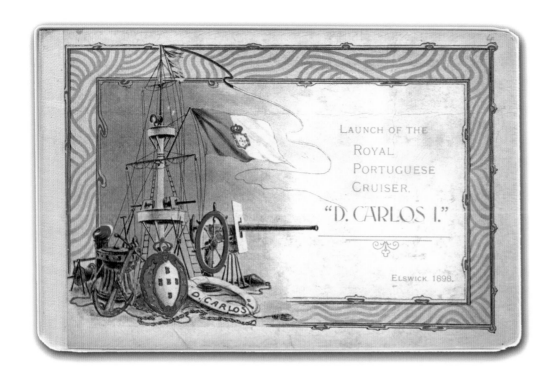

LAUNCH OF THE

ROYAL
PORTUGUESE
CRUISER.

"D. CARLOS I."

ELSWICK. 1898.

The Royal Portuguese cruiser *D. Carlos I*, built by Sir W.G. Armstrong, Whitworth & Co. Ltd., was launched from the Elswick Shipyard on May 5, 1898 by Madame Capello.

Principal dimensions
Length: 360ft
Breadth 47ft 3ins
Draft, mean 17ft 6ins
Displacement in tons 4,100

Armament
4 6-in quick firing guns
8 4-7-in quick firing guns
12 3 pdr quick firing guns
4 machine guns
5 torpedo tubes (3 submerged)

HIJMS *Takasago*, built by Sir W.G. Armstrong, Whitworth & Co. Ltd., was launched from the Low Walker Shipyard on May 18, 1897 by Miss Noble.

A programme of variety entertainment by the crew was arranged for May 23. The shorthand pencilled on the programme may have been written by a local reporter writing his impressions of the event.

Principal dimensions
Length 360 ft
Breadth 46ft 6ins
Draft, mean 17ft
Displacement, in tons 4,160

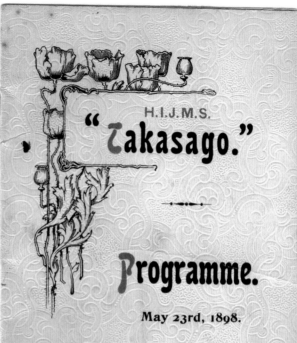

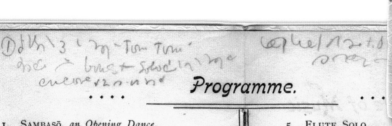

Programme.

1. SAMBASŌ, *an Opening Dance.*

2. SLEIGHT OF HAND.

3. FENCING.

4. CHIUSHINGURA, *Scene* 7.

   This is one of the scenes from "Chiusingura," better known in England as "Forty-seven Ronins." The chief of the Ronins feigns debauchery to put the enemy off their guard. Some of the Ronins not being able to fathom their chief's intentions, believe that he has really forgotten the vow they have made to avenge the death of their master, and with difficulty restrain themselves from committing some act of violence on him. They get to understand him better subsequently, and the scene closes in a satisfactory manner.

5. FLUTE SOLO.

6. CHON KINA.

7. BAKEJIZŌ, *or the Living Statue* (a farce).

   A sculptor receives an order to make a statue in a single day, who, finding himself unequal to the task within the prescribed time, persuades a friend to impersonate the statue for a certain sum of money, and duly instals him on a pedestal in the country roadside, in place of the statue. Presently the village yokels come along, and after admiring the workmanship and commenting on its being so extremely lifelike, commence to cut all sorts of antics. The man who represents the statue, being unable to refrain from joining them, descends from the pedestal, and the general fiasco follows.

8. DANCE IN COSTUME.

Launch of the First-Class
Armoured Cruiser
"TOKIWA"
For the . . .
Imperial
Japanese
Navy.

Elswick, 1898.

HIJMS *Tokiwa*, built for the Imperial Japanese Navy by Sir W.G. Armstrong, Whitworth & Co. Ltd., was launched from the Elswick Shipyard on July 6, 1898 by Madame Kato.

Principal dimensions
Length 408ft
Breadth 67ft
Draft 24ft 4.25ins
Displacement in tons 9,700

Armament
4 8-in BL guns in two barbettes
14 6-in QF guns (10 in casements)
12 12 pdr QF guns
7 2.5 pdr QF guns
5 torpedo tubes (4 submerged)

United States cruiser *Albany*, built by Sir W.G. Armstrong, Whitworth & Co. Ltd., was launched at the Elswick Shipyard on Saturday January 14, 1899 by Mrs Colwell.

Principal dimensions
Length 330ft
Breadth 43ft 9 ins
Draft 16ft 10ins
Displacement in tons about 3,450

Armament
6 6-in quick firing guns
4 4.7in quick firing guns
10 6-pdr quick firing guns
4 1-pdr quick firing guns
4 Maxim guns
2 12-pdr field guns
3 torpedo tubes

Ermack (*Yermack*), built by Sir W.G. Armstrong, Whitworth & Co. Ltd., was launched from the Low Walker Shipyard on Saturday October 29, 1898 by Madame Vasilieff.

Principal dimensions
Length 305ft
Breadth 71ft
Depth 42ft 6ins
Displacement 8,000 tons
Indicated horse power 10,000

The Royal Mail and passenger turbine steamer *Viking* was built for the Isle of Man Steam Packet Company Limited. She was built by Sir W.G. Armstrong, Whitworth & Co. Ltd., and launched from the Low Walker shipyard on March 7, 1905 by Miss Woodhead.

Principal dimensions
Length overall 361ft
Length between perpendiculars 350ft
Breadth extreme 42ft
Depth moulded 17ft 3 ins
Speed 22 knots

The passenger ferry Viking was built for service between the Isle of Man and Lancashire. Launched at Low Walker in 1905, Viking served as a seaplane carrier during the First World War and a troopship during the Second. She sailed on her last voyage between the Isle of Man and the mainland in 1954 after a career lasting 49 years.

Launch of the Royal Norwegian Armourclad "Norge"
Elswick Shipyard. 1900.

Royal Norwegian armourclad *Norge*, built by Sir W.G. Armstrong, Whitworth & Co. Ltd., was launched from the Elswick Shipyard on March 31, 1900 by Mrs Saxton Noble.

Principal dimensions
Length 290ft
Breadth 50ft 6ins
Depth 26ft 6ins
Draft 16ft 6ins
Displacement in tons 3,850

Armament
2 21-c/m quick firing guns
6 15-c/m quick firing guns
8 12-pdr quick firing guns
6 3-pdr quick firing guns
2 torpedo tubes (submerged)

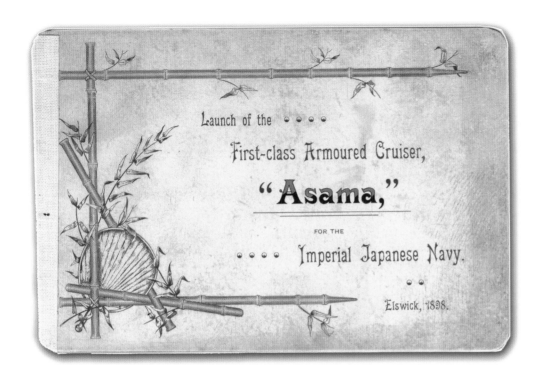

Launch of the . . . .
First-class Armoured Cruiser,
"**Asama**,"
FOR THE
. . . . Imperial Japanese Navy.

Elswick, 1898.

HIJMS *Asama* was built for the Imperial Japanese Navy by Sir W.G. Armstrong, Whitworth & Co. Ltd., and launched from the Elswick Shipyard on March 22, 1898 by Madame Arakawa.

Principal dimensions
Length 408ft
Breadth 67ft
Draft 24ft 4.25ins
Displacement in tons 9,700

Armament
4 8-in BL guns, in 2 barbettes
14 6-in QF guns (10 in casements)
12 12-pdr quick firing guns
7 2.5-pdr quick firing guns
5 torpedo tubes (4 submerged)

LAUNCH OF
H.I.M. The Sultan's
YACHT
"*Erthogroul*"
BY
HER EXCELLENCY THE
Turkish Ambassadress.
ELSWICK SHIPYARD.
December 30th, 1903.

HIM The Sultan's twin screw steam yacht *Erthogroul*, built by Sir W.G. Armstrong, Whitworth & Co. Ltd, was launched from the Elswick Shipyard on December 30, 1903 by Her Excellency the Turkish Ambassadress.

Principal dimensions
Length (between perpendiculars) 260ft
Breadth, moulded 27ft 6ins
Depth, moulded 15ft
Draft, mean 10ft

Armament
8 3-pdr quick firing guns

Photos of Angara by David Saunders, School of Historical Studies, University of Newcastle upon Tyne

Angara (see page 87), a passenger-carrying icebreaker, was constructed at Low Walker, dismantled, shipped to St Petersburg, then transported to Lake Baikal to begin service in 1900. Still surviving, today she has been converted to a museum ship moored on the icy Angara River in Irkutsk. These photographs were taken in 2006.

Togo's Heroes at St James' Park, April 1906.

In April 1906 Japanese sailors arrived on Tyneside to take delivery of the battleship Kashima which had been launched at Elswick the previous year. The Kashima was the last warship to be built at the yard for the Imperial Japanese Navy. It was the end of an era, for it was no longer necessary for Japan to have such vessels built abroad. The Land of the Rising Sun was now able to construct its own warships. More than 100 men of the Kashima, and a group of officers watched a football match at St James' Park between Newcastle and Stoke during their visit to the city. The crew spent the afternoon of Tuesday 24 April looking around the city centre. When they arrived at the football ground they found welcoming messages displayed in Japanese. The men had tea with the club directors and were cheered by the crowd as they took their places on the stand. Many of the sailors had fought in the Battle of Tsushima in 1905 and were regarded as heroes. Newcastle scored a resounding 5-0 victory in front of a crowd of 12,000.

The Mystery of HMS Wasp

A delicately sculptured fountain is situated above the old harbour at Cullercoats, North Tyneside. It is dedicated to the memory of a local man and his Elswick-built ship, Lieutenant Commander Bryan John Huthwaite Adamson, captain of the gunboat HMS *Wasp*.

Cullercoats born and bred, Lieutenant Commander Adamson was in his mid-thirties when he was appointed to the newly-built *Wasp*. She was his first, only and last command. In a naval career dating back to 1866, when he left the Britannia Naval College, he had served in many parts of the world. His entire career had been spent aboard ships of the transitional period between sail and steam. All of them had engines and most carried a good spread of canvas and were capable of sustaining ocean passages under sail alone. This was often done when winds were favourable to conserve their coal bunkers. Managing a ship with the barquetine sailing rig of the *Wasp* as well as an engine would have presented few problems to him.

The memorial fountain to Bryan Adamson.

HMS *Wasp* was launched at Elswick on September 13, 1886. The number 13 has some superstitious associations among seafarers. So should the name *Wasp*. Just why the Admiralty had chosen such a name for a newly-built gunboat is a mystery. Only two years before the launch another gunboat bearing the name *Wasp* had struck an isolated rock off the west coast of Ireland and gone down with 52 of her crew, including the captain. Only six had been saved. The details of this disaster must have been fresh in the minds of many seafaring men as the new *Wasp* slid down the ways into the Tyne.

She left the river on December 30, 1886. In April the following year the *Wasp* was commissioned for service in Chinese waters and on May 21 set out on the long passage towards Shanghai. The gunboat's route took her through the Mediterranean and the Suez Canal, then down the Red Sea from where her crew, in letters home, complained of the very hot weather. Then it was across the Indian Ocean to Singapore, which was to be her last stop before heading northwards towards her final destination.

By the time Singapore was reached, the satisfaction and novelty of a first command had soured for Lieutenant Commander Adamson. His feelings were expressed in a letter written to his mother: 'I don't care much for my command; things may turn out better, but with the two inexperienced officers I have to assist me I am captain, first lieutenant and navigator all in one. Since leaving England I have never been in bed before daylight at sea.'

Crew member John Roach, a carpenter, made an even more serious allegation about his immediate superior in a letter to his father. He stated that the mate he was under had never been aboard a ship before and was altogether incompetent for the job. John Roach went on to say that the *Wasp* was undermanned and the seamen terribly hard-worked.

The problem of undermanning had also troubled Adamson. While the *Wasp* was at Sheerness he had petitioned his superiors for 12 additional able seamen. Only eight had been

The Rattler and the Wasp on the stocks at Elswick. The Wasp is on the right, in an earlier stage of construction.

Tyne & Wear Archives & Museums

allocated. The situation was aggravated still further on the passage out. An accident aloft had robbed him of the crew member he described as his 'smartest seaman'. This man had to be landed in Ceylon (now Sri Lanka). He was lucky.

It cannot have been a very happy ship which stood out from Singapore on September 10, 1887. There were 80 souls on board. Seventy-three of these made up the *Wasp's* regular complement. The rest were men on their way to join other ships on the China Station.

They expected to reach Shanghai around September 21 but never did. For they and the *Wasp* simply disappeared without trace.

It was thought that she foundered while traversing the South China Sea during a typhoon which was known to have been raging at the time. Other shipping certainly suffered. On September 15, the Chinese transport vessel *Waylee* was driven ashore on the Pescadores with the loss of 285 lives.

Five days later the British barque *Oxford* came to grief on the coast of Bataan in the Philippines and the steamship *Anton* had her decks swept by an enormous sea which carried overboard the second mate and 24 Chinese.

As the days passed and with no news of the *Wasp*, the anxious naval authorities at Hong Kong sent warships fanning out into the South China Sea to look for her. The cruiser *Leander* and gunboat *Cockchafer* went to the Paracel Islands. *Firebrand*, a tiny 450-ton gunboat, concentrated on the Pratas Shoal.

From Singapore the cable steamer *Recorder* combed the islands to the north of that place as well as the coast of Cochin China and Hainan Island. Another ship which became involved in the search was the screw corvette HMS *Calliope*. In later years the *Calliope* was moored at Elswick as the training ship of the Tyne Division of the Royal Naval Volunteer Reserve. Like all the others, she found nothing.

The search continued throughout October and into November. The *Wasp's* sister ship, the Elswick-built HMS *Rattler*, was sent to search the Cocos Islands and other vessels from Singapore were 'making inquiries'.

Finally, at the beginning of December, the Admiralty published the following notice: 'All hopes for the safety of HMS *Wasp* having now been relinquished, directions have been given that her books are to be considered closed on December 6, 1887, and the balance of the wages due up to that date is to be paid to the representatives of the officers and men.'

A few days later, Dr Frank Rennie, a close friend of Lieutenant Commander Adamson, proposed that a memorial drinking fountain be erected in Cullercoats where Lieutenant Commander Adamson 'was so well known and beloved'.

An impression of Wasp at sea.

Loss of the Cobra

The invention of the marine steam turbine engine by Tyneside-based Sir Charles Parsons was to revolutionise the propulsion of warships and passenger liners. In 1897 Parsons had cleverly demonstrated the capabilities of his turbine engine by staging a display of speed at Queen Victoria's Diamond Jubilee Fleet Review. His long, sleek steam yacht *Turbinia*, built on the Tyne, had raced past the warships assembled in Spithead at a speed of 34.5 knots.

However, even before this display, Armstrong Whitworth had been interested in the idea of fitting the turbine engine in one of its vessels. The company made the decision to install the machinery in a torpedo boat destroyer which would be built 'on spec' in the hope of finding a buyer. HMS *Cobra*, as the ship was to become, was launched at Elswick on June 28, 1899.

Her structural arrangements were based on those of two other vessels built at Elswick for the Admiralty in 1895. However, there was one major difference. The turbine machinery of the *Cobra* weighed 183 tons. That was 73 tons more than the machinery in the other two ships and 30 tons heavier than had been envisaged. But designer Philip Watts was later to state that 'a margin for such an eventuality had been incorporated in the original design'.

The *Cobra* was offered for sale to the Admiralty in December, 1899. However, the naval authorities were unhappy

Cobra undergoing sea trials c.1900-01.

with certain aspects of the ship and demanded that modifications be made before they would accept her. The main requirement was that her upper deck be strengthened. This was duly carried out.

The *Cobra* had been launched two months before HMS *Viper*, another turbine-driven torpedo boat destroyer which was built by Hawthorn Leslie of Hebburn. But the *Viper* was completed ahead of the *Cobra* and became the world's first turbine-driven warship. This distinction would have gone to the *Cobra* had it not been for a collier ship running into her as she lay alongside her fitting-out quay at Elswick. The damage took seven months to repair.

On May 8, 1900, the *Cobra* was sold to the Admiralty for £63,500. In June she clocked up a speed of 34.89 knots on trials. It was not until September the following year that the ship was ready to leave her builders. There were 79 men aboard her for the run from the Tyne to Portsmouth where she was to be armed and commissioned. Twenty-four were from the North-East – mainly employees of Armstrong Whitworth and of Parsons, the turbine builders. Included among them were two distinguished engineers, Magnus Sandison and Robert Barnard.

Sandison had been superintendent engineer at Elswick since the yard was first opened. He was the designer of a special type of marine engine known as the 'six-crank'. Robert Barnard was the manager of the Parsons company which was

Magnus Sandison, photographed the day before the Cobra sailed from the Tyne.

based on the Tyne. He assisted in the design of *Turbinia* and had supervised her construction. He had also been closely involved with the building of the *Cobra, Viper* and the Clyde steamer *King Edward*, the first turbine-driven passenger vessel.

At 5pm on September 9, 1901, the *Cobra* sailed from the Tyne. To begin with all went well and she ran along at 17 knots. But as the night wore on the weather began to deteriorate. The new torpedo boat destroyer started to roll so heavily that it was impossible for the men to work in her cramped stoke-hold. Speed had to be reduced to four or five knots. When daylight came it was possible to increase speed slightly.

At 7am a lightship was sighted on the starboard bow. Sandison made his way forward to try to identify it. Suddenly there was a distinct shock as if the ship had 'gone over something'. Within seconds the *Cobra* had broken in two.

The crew of the Outer Dowsing Light Vessel off the Lincolnshire coast had watched with interest as the *Cobra* came into view. Their interest turned to horror as she suddenly seemed to blow up in a cloud of steam and smoke.

They thought she was the victim of a boiler explosion. Immediately danger signals were hoisted aboard the lightship. Four guns were fired in an effort to attract the attention of a passing steamer, but she held her course until out of sight, unaware of the disaster she was leaving behind.

At 4.30pm Yarmouth Herring Boat *No. 15* was drifting for

fish near the Outer Dowsing Buoy. As she went along with the tide *No.15* found herself amongst a group of bodies all wearing lifebelts which 'had proved to be death traps; some of the men were floating with their feet uppermost'. The bodies of four sailors and two civilians were hauled aboard the fishing boat. Her skipper, John Smith, made for Grimsby to report the disaster. On the way, he spoke to the lightship men. By this time more bodies were floating past the anchored vessel.

At 6pm the P & O steamer *Harlington* was heading north on passage from London to Middlesbrough under the command of a Captain Young. He was chatting to his chief engineer, Mr James of Newcastle, when they sighted a small boat a couple of miles to the south of them. Course was altered to investigate. The boat proved to be the *Cobra's* 14ft dinghy with 12 men on board. They were the only survivors. Sandison and Barnard were not among them.

A court martial to try the surviving crew and inquire into the loss of the *Cobra* was convened aboard HMS *Victory* at Portsmouth in October 1901. Much of the evidence centred around the construction of the vessel. Philip Watts told the court a number of sea trials had been made in bad weather and the *Cobra* had come through these in a most satisfactory manner. Naval construction officials spoke well of her.

The mate in charge of the Outer Dowsing Light Vessel, Samuel Hambling, faced an awkward question at the hearing. The lightship was equipped with two boats, one 20ft and one 14ft long. He had a crew of six, all experienced boatmen. Hambling told the court there was too much wind and sea to launch a boat. This brought the question from the court: 'You say there was too much wind and sea for you to use your boat. How do you account for the fact that a 14ft boat of the *Cobra*

with 12 men on board succeeded in remaining in it for 11 hours?'

Hambling quoted his instructions which forbade him from leaving the lightship on any pretext. The matter does not seem to have been pursued any further, but his decision not to put out a boat may well have troubled his conscience for the rest of his life.

The findings of the court martial were announced on October 16, 1901. They were not complimentary to Armstrong Whitworth. It was found that the *Cobra* did not touch the seabed or meet any obstruction; nor was her loss due to any error of navigation but was attributable to the 'weakness' of the ship. The court also found that the *Cobra* was weaker than other destroyers, and it was 'to be regretted that she was purchased into His Majesty's Service'.

No blame was attached to any of the survivors and they were fully acquitted. Torpedo-Coxswain Francis Barnes was praised for the way in which he had handled the dinghy and the survivors on board.

Sixty-seven men had lost their lives in the disaster. Many of them were from Tyneside. A fund was set up to help their dependants. Armstrong Whitworth contributed £1,000.

Fate was no kinder to the *Cobra's* sister, HMS *Viper*. This vessel also had a short-lived career. She was wrecked on rocks near Alderney in the Channel Islands in August 1901, although there was no loss of life. The Admiralty never again named a surface ship after a snake.

Disease on Board

Ships are usually remembered for such factors as tragedy, novelty, fighting reputation, luxury speed or good looks. However, the Elswick-built cruiser *Barroso* should perhaps be remembered for a disease – beri-beri.

Built for the Brazilian Navy, the ship was launched on August 25, 1896, by Madame Sisson, wife of Commander Sisson, secretary of the Brazilian Naval Commission in Europe. 'The ceremony was performed under the most happy and auspicious circumstance,' reported the *Newcastle Daily Journal*. 'The weather was delightfully fine and in consequence a very large number of ladies and gentlemen were present, the former being costumed in the brightest and most picturesque of summer garbs.'

The *Barroso*, or *Almirante Barroso* as she is sometimes referred to, carried six 6-inch guns and four 4.8-inch quick-firing guns. Driven by triple expansion engines, she was capable of 20.5 knots.

Nowadays, beri-beri is usually only met with in countries of the world where the staple diet is polished rice, but until relatively recent years it was frequently met with at sea. Indeed, it was as much a seaman's disease as the more publicised scurvy, and like that condition it is also caused by a vitamin deficiency.

The disease occurs in two forms. There is the dry type, which gives rise to paralysis and severe pains in the arms and legs, and the wet type, which is characterised by marked oedema and heart failure. Dry or wet, both are serious conditions.

For part of her career, the *Barroso* was bedevilled by this scourge. It first occurred amongst her crew in 1904. Four years later there was another outbreak. At the time beri-beri was reported to be prevalent in North Brazil, the *Barroso*'s home territory.

On July 3, 1909, the vessel left Rio de Janeiro with a crew of 434 on board. A call was made at Recife. Then she steamed across the South Atlantic to St Vincent in the Cape Verde Islands, where she stayed for a short period before heading northwards to Las Palmas in the Canary Islands.

Forty days after leaving Rio she put into Plymouth. While there, two seamen complained of an illness which the ship's surgeon diagnosed as beri-beri. From Plymouth the *Barroso* continued her northward journey towards the Tyne, probably in connection with the commissioning of the two scout cruisers, *Bahia* and *Rio Grande do Sul,* being built at Elswick.

While in the river three more of her crew went down with the illness. Dr W.E. Harker, the Medical Officer of Health on the Tyne, had these men taken to the floating hospital at Jarrow Slake. Soon they were joined by more of their shipmates until no fewer than 40 had been admitted to the same hospital.

It is interesting to note the treatment received by these men.

To begin with rice was eliminated from their diet. Ample quantities of fresh vegetables, fruit and milk were given. Additional measures were also taken. 'Suspecting that the toxin might gain entrance by the alimentary tract,' wrote Dr Harker, 'I have given an intestinal disinfectant followed in the morning by a mild aperient of sulphur of soda. As a general tonic quinine with strychnine in small doses appears to do good.'

In the light of more modern knowledge it is probable that the change of diet did more good than Dr Harker's additional treatment, but the fact remains that there

The cruiser Barroso, launched for the Brazilian Navy in 1896. Crew members were affected by the disease beri-beri.

was only one fatality. None of the officers were affected. At the time this was largely accounted for by their better standard of accommodation, but the more varied diet available to them would have been nearer the truth.

Beri-beri was not confined to foreign vessels. Four years after the *Barroso*'s visit to the Tyne, a North Shields-owned barquetine, the *Sound of Jura*, was towed into the Cape Verde Islands by the Newcastle tramp steamer *Uskmoor* after being found near derelict in the South Atlantic with most of her crew incapacitated by the disease.

The *Barroso*, like most Elswick ships of the 1890s, was designed by Philip Watts, who was knighted in 1905. Sir Philip had succeeded Sir William White as naval architect and general manager of the yard in 1885. Sir William left Tyneside to become Admiralty Director of Naval Construction. Sir Philip followed in his predecessor's footsteps for a second time when in 1902 he took over the same post at the Admiralty. Leading Elswick naval architects after 1902 included Josiah Perrett and Sir Eustace H. Tennyson D'Eyncourt.

The *Barroso* was one of a considerable number of ships built at the yard for South American navies. For example, the Argentine cruiser *25 de Mayo* (*Veinticinco de Mayo*) was the first of five vessels launched at Elswick for the Argentine Navy. The ship was designed by Phillip Watts.

The *25 de Mayo* was named after a memorable day in her country's history, May 25, 1810, when Argentine nationalists unseated the Spanish viceroy at La Plata and so helped to start a trend which ultimately brought down the Spanish South American empire.

The ship was launched on May 5, 1890, but completion was delayed by a joiners' strike. When she eventually did emerge from the Tyne her performance was very impressive. During trials in November 1890 she achieved a top speed of 22.47 knots. The *Newcastle Daily Leader* proclaimed that 'speeds realised on these trials have never before been reached by any ship previously built'. On January 29, 1891, the *25 de Mayo* undertook gunnery trials off the Tyne. A number of foreign guests were invited to witness these, including representatives of the USA, Russia and Turkey.

While completion of the *25 de Mayo* had been slow, instalment payments for her from the Argentine government were equally slow in coming to Armstrong Mitchell. She was still at Elswick at the end of April, 1891. Her crew had arrived and her commander-designate, Captain Ramirez, asked that they might be allowed to sleep on board. Permission to do this was reluctantly granted, for it was normally a strict company rule not to allow this. It was made clear that the ship remained the property of the company and should not hoist the Argentine flag or leave the river.

In May the *25 de Mayo* was still held up in the Tyne, but this time moored off Jarrow, awaiting payment of the final instalment. Eventually, all was settled and in August the fine new cruiser sailed for Argentina, calling at Rio de Janeiro on the way.

Perhaps the most unusually named of Elswick's South American ships was the cruiser *O'Higgins* (see launch card on page 38), completed for Chile in 1898. She was named after Bernardo O'Higgins, a Chilean patriot of Irish descent who led his country to freedom from Spanish rule. The ship is sometimes called the *Almirante O'Higgins* or *General O'Higgins*.

The cruiser was launched on May 18, 1897, by Doña Mercedes Valdes de Barro Luco, wife of the Chilean minister in London. The event was watched by naval officers from several nations with ships under construction at Elswick. They included captains from Japan, Brazil, Portugal and China.

The *O'Higgins* was fitted with three immensely tall funnels, placed close together slightly forward of amidships, which gave her a distinctive appearance.

During the same year in which this ship was launched the Armstrong Mitchell business underwent a further transformation when it amalgamated with the Manchester-

The launch of the cruiser O'Higgins at the Elswick Yard in 1897.

based armaments firm of Sir Joseph Whitworth to become Sir W.G. Armstrong, Whitworth and Co. Ltd.

Meanwhile, Lord Armstrong spent increasing amounts of time at Cragside, his mansion in the rugged Northumberland countryside at Rothbury. He died there on December 27, 1900, at the age of 90. Sadly he and his wife, Lady Margaret Armstrong, were childless. Armstrong's business partner, gun technology expert and former artillery officer Sir Andrew Noble, succeeded him as chairman of the company.

William Armstrong had been a great benefactor of Newcastle, his native city, contributing funds towards the building of the Hancock Natural History Museum and to Newcastle Infirmary. In the early 1870s he donated money for the building of a new operating theatre at the infirmary and in 1885 helped to finance the construction of an additional wing to the hospital known as the Ravensworth Wards.

In 1878 he gave 26 acres of his land on his Jesmond estate in Newcastle to the people of the city for their recreation and pleasure. This land, situated between Jesmond Dene and the present day Heaton Park, would become known as Armstrong Park.

Then, in 1883 he crowned this gift with another. This time he gave his land at Jesmond Dene to the people as a park. To this day it remains one of Newcastle's most beautiful and distinctive spots and is a haven of peace just minutes from the city centre.

Lord Armstrong also gave £3,000 towards a fund set up to build a new hospital, which became the Royal Victoria Infirmary, opened in 1906. His great nephew, William Watson-Armstrong, inherited his fortune. In his memory, Watson-Armstrong gave £100,000 towards the building of the new infirmary. It was a third of the cost of constructing and equipping the hospital. Money created by the production of guns and warships capable of destroying life was thus by an extreme irony used to save lives and relieve suffering.

The death of the great inventor and philanthropist did not affect warship building at Elswick. In 1903, the yard launched the Turkish cruiser *Abdul Hamid*. She was renamed *Hamidieh* in 1908 and went on to have a long life. Designed by one of the yard's accomplished naval architects, Josiah Perrett, the *Hamidieh* sank at least three ships during her career. Turkey's long-lived cruiser did not go the breaker's yard until the 1960s.

The steam yacht *Erthogroul* (see launch card on page 47) was launched at the yard in the same year as the *Hamidieh*. The vessel had been ordered by the Sultan of Turkey. Internal fittings were by Waring and Sons (later to become Waring and Gillow Ltd.) who had also been responsible for the interiors of the British and German royal yachts, the *Victoria and Albert* and *Hohenzollern* respectively. The Turkish Imperial saloon was framed and panelled in mahogany and gold. The furniture and piano matched the panelling.

Erthogroul was launched by the wife of the Turkish ambassador, Masurus Pacha. Among those present at the ceremony was the vessel's designer, Josiah Perrett.

During the First World War, Elswick-built warships played their role in the unfolding conflict, two with tragic consequences.

The first of these was the battle-cruiser HMS *Invincible*, which had been launched in 1907 and which, with her sister, HMS *Inflexible*, sank the German armoured cruisers *Scharnhorst* and *Gneisenau* at the Battle of the Falklands in December 1914. But the *Invincible* was to meet disaster at the

Battle of Jutland on May 31 1916 when she was sunk by German warships with the loss of 1,020 lives. Only six survived. These lucky men were picked up by a British destroyer.

Equally ill-fated was the Elswick-built cruiser HMS *Hampshire*, which had been completed in 1905. She took part at Jutland but was lost only a few days after the battle. On June 5, 1916, the 22-knot *Hampshire* left Scapa Flow in the Orkneys during a strong gale. She was carrying Lord Kitchener on a wartime mission to Russia.

But on the evening of the same day the cruiser struck a mine in heavy seas and sank in a short space of time. Kitchener, his staff and most

The Brazilian battleship Rio de Janeiro alongside the fitting out quay at Elswick, 1913. She later became the British ship HMS Agincourt and fought at Jutland.

of the ship's crew lost their lives. The mine had been laid by a U-boat.

The two largest warships to fight with the British Fleet at Jutland were also launched at the Elswick Yard. They were the battleships HMS *Agincourt* and HMS *Canada*. Both had originally been ordered by South American navies, but Britain took them over for service during the First World War.

Agincourt was launched under the name *Rio de Janeiro* for Brazil in 1913 and was equipped with no less than 14 12-inch guns in seven turrets. However, Brazil had financial problems and was unable to pay for this vast battleship. She was therefore sold to Turkey and renamed the *Sultan Osman I*.

Meanwhile, the vessel was moved down river to the newly-opened Walker Naval Yard in the East End of Newcastle, which the company had set up to eventually replace the Elswick Yard. Every effort was being made to deliver the ship on time for the Turkish Navy. Men worked on the ship at Walker throughout the Newcastle Race Week holidays in the early summer of 1914.

Several weeks afterwards came a dramatic development. The yard workmen must have been surprised when British soldiers boarded the vessel shortly before the outbreak of the First World War in August 1914. She was taken over for service with the Royal Navy.

Turkey seems to have missed sailing out of the river with its 22-knot battleship by a whisker. A Turkish captain and crew had arrived in the Tyne to man the *Sultan Osman I,* but when they

The launch of the Chilean battleship Almirante Latorre at the Elswick Yard in 1913.

attempted to board the vessel they found her guarded by the soldiers.

The sailors had no choice but to return home on another ship. Britain renamed its newly-acquired 'giant' HMS *Agincourt* and transferred her to the Grand Fleet at Scapa Flow in the Orkneys. She survived the war.

Chile had also ordered a battleship from Elswick. Originally named the *Almirante Latorre*, she was launched in

1913 and carried ten 14-inch guns. However, the outbreak of the First World War brought a halt to work on the vessel and she was taken over by Britain in September 1914. Britain then agreed to buy her from Chile and work was re-started. Completed in late 1915, the ship was renamed HMS *Canada*.

Surviving the conflict, in 1920 the 23-knot vessel was re-purchased by Chile, who gave her back the name *Almirante Latorre*. Serving many years in the Chilean Navy, the former *Canada* was the longest surviving battleship which had fought at Jutland. She went to the breaker's yard in 1959.

Jutland also witnessed the debut of the battleship HMS *Malaya*, which was the first vessel to be built at Armstrong Whitworth's Walker Naval Yard. The yard had opened for production in 1913.

Although the Elswick Yard's output consisted overwhelmingly of warships, it did launch a few merchant vessels. These included four oil tankers, a passenger cargo steamer, a cargo steamer and a cableship.

Elswick's last vessel was the aircraft carrier HMS *Eagle*, launched in 1918. She was moved down river to the Walker Naval Yard for fitting out. The days of colourful launchings at the old yard were over.

However, the Elswick Works, together with the adjoining works at Scotswood, continued as a vast centre of arms production and was to play a leading role in manufacturing guns and tanks for Britain during both world wars. But the Elswick Shipyard never reopened.

The Walker Naval Yard now became Armstrong Whitworth's sole warship building base on the Tyne and would add merchant shipbuilding to its achievements. The yard's output would include elegant passenger liners and sturdy cargo carriers as well as cruisers, destroyers and two battleships, HMS *Nelson* and HMS *King George V*.

The Walker Naval Yard's first merchant vessel was the refrigerated cargo carrier *Tairoa*, launched in 1920. This major yard came under the ownership of Vickers-Armstrongs Ltd at the end of 1927. It was to go on launching ships until well after the Second World War, including the passenger liner *Empress of Canada*, completed in 1961.

Armstrong's Yards Timeline

1810 William Armstrong born in Shieldfield, Newcastle.

1847 Armstrong and four business partners set up the Elswick Works in Newcastle for the manufacture of hydraulic cranes and other water-powered machinery.

1852 Charles Mitchell sets up a shipyard at Low Walker, Newcastle.

1853 First vessel launched at Low Walker, the *Havilah*.

1859 William Armstrong knighted.

1867 Sir William and Charles Mitchell agree that Mitchell's Low Walker yard should construct warships which will be fitted with guns manufactured at Armstrong's Elswick Works.

1882 Sir William and Charles Mitchell agree to amalgamate businesses to form Sir W.G. Armstrong, Mitchell and Co. Ltd.

1884 The new company opens a shipyard at Elswick. It is agreed that the Elswick Yard will concentrate on building mainly warships and Low Walker mainly merchant vessels.

1885 First vessel launched at the Elswick Yard, the Austro-Hungarian torpedo cruiser *Panther*.

1887 Sir William created 1st Baron Armstrong of Cragside.

1895 Charles Mitchell dies.

1897 The business amalgamates with Joseph Whitworth of Manchester to form Sir W.G. Armstrong, Whitworth & Co. Ltd.

1900 Lord Armstrong dies.

1913 Armstrong Whitworth's new Walker Naval Yard, Newcastle, opens.

1918 Last warship launched at Elswick Yard, the aircraft carrier HMS *Eagle*.

1927 Armstrong Whitworth amalgamates some of its most important business interests with concerns owned by Vickers Ltd., of Barrow-in-Furness, to form Vickers-Armstrongs Ltd.

1947 Last ship launched at Low Walker Yard, the cargo vessel *Zarian*, later renamed the *Lokoja Palm*.

Low Walker Launchings

The Low Walker Shipyard in the East End of Newcastle, which had merged with Armstrong's company in 1882, had been founded long before the one at Elswick. It was set up by Aberdeen-born Charles Mitchell in 1852-53. This enterprising man had arrived in Newcastle from Scotland ten years earlier, and had entered the employment of John Coutts, a pioneer of iron shipbuilding on the river who also owned a yard at Low Walker.

Charles Mitchell, who was a skilled draughtsman, stayed with Coutts for two years, gaining valuable experience, and then moved south to London to work for a firm of marine engineers, Maudslay, Sons and Field, of Lambeth.

In 1852, however, he returned to the Tyne to set up his own yard at Low Walker next to the one which had been operated by Coutts, who

Charles Mitchell.

had by then moved on.

On March 20, 1853, an advertisement appeared in the *Newcastle Daily Journal* stating that 'the splendid new clipper ship *Havilah*' would leave Newcastle Quay on April 7 bound for Melbourne, Australia, with a call being made at London on the way. The voyage to Melbourne was partly aimed at those potential passengers seeking to make their fortunes in the gold fields of Australia.

The *Havilah* was the first ship in a long line of vessels built at the Low Walker Yard by Charles Mitchell & Co., and the company's successors, Armstrong Mitchell and Armstrong Whitworth.

The barque-rigged *Havilah* had been launched on February 12, 1853, and although carrying a spread of sails, she was also equipped with an engine linked to a propeller. The engine had been supplied by Messrs. Hawks, Crawshay & Sons, of Gateshead.

The vessel went on to become a pioneer steamship in Australian waters and changed ownership several times. She was broken up at Sydney in 1911 after a long and useful life.

At the same time as the *Havilah* was being constructed, Charles Mitchell had another propeller-driven ship on the stocks at Low Walker. She was the *Cagliari,* launched in October, 1853, for Sardinian owners and intended for the Mediterranean trade. Rigged as a three-masted schooner, her engines were supplied by Robert Stephenson & Co., of Newcastle.

Two other ships were also completed at Low Walker during that first year of business. They were the steam-driven colliers *Vulcan* and *Will o' the Wisp*, which were employed taking coal from the North East to Ireland.

Charles Mitchell's new shipyard had clearly got off to a good start and soon it was a flourishing concern. In the early years of its life steam colliers proved to be a mainstay of the order books. Of the first 16 ships built, 11 were for the coal trade. It was a time when the old sailing collier brigs were rapidly being replaced by screw steamers which were faster, more reliable and had a greater cargo capacity than the sailing colliers.

In January 1856 one of the Mitchell-built colliers, the *General Codrington*, made the round passage from the Tyne to

London and back in four days, seven hours, which at that date was the fastest passage ever made on the route. She had carried 600 tons of coal. It would have taken two sailing colliers about a month to equal this performance.

However, not all the yard's early ships had successful careers. For example, the collier *Will o' the Wisp's* life was cut short when in February 1855 she hit a rock off the eastern coast of Ireland in a snowstorm. There were no survivors. She had been bound from Newcastle to Dublin with coals and was also carrying passengers.

On February 23, 1856, Mitchell's yard was the scene of a triple launch witnessed by a large number of spectators. The first vessel to slide down the ways was the 76-ton screw steam yacht *George Robert*, built for Mr George Bidder, of London. The engine for the vessel was supplied by Messrs. Robert Stephenson & Co., of Newcastle.

Next came the *Paris*, a 200ft-long steamer intended for service carrying passengers and cargo between Hamburg and Le Havre. The third ship was the *Eupatoria*, a steam collier whose engines also came from the Stephenson company's works.

In May 1854 Charles Mitchell had married Anne Swan, of West Farm, Walker, Newcastle, and the couple moved into a house close to the Low Walker Yard. Later, after a spell in the south of England, they settled in Jesmond, Newcastle, where the financially successful Charles bought a mansion which he named Jesmond Towers. Many years later it was to become the main building of La Sagesse School, which closed in 2008.

Charles and Ann had three sons, but only one survived, Charles William, who became an accomplished artist.

Jesmond Towers was, and still is, situated near to Jesmond Dene Road, where Lord Armstrong and Sir Andrew Noble also had residences. All three homes were close to one another. Armstrong's house was named Jesmond Dean (the more usual spelling 'dene' seems to have been avoided for some reason). This property is no longer in existence. Sir Andrew Noble's residence, Jesmond Dene House, is now a hotel and restaurant.

Low Walker shipyard in 1857.

By about 1860 Charles Mitchell's brother-in-law, Henry F. Swan, had joined the company as an employee, eventually becoming a partner in the business. The Low Walker Yard went from strength to strength, in particular pioneering the development of oil tankers and producing a wide variety of other vessels.

Although undergoing several changes of ownership and experiencing the effects of the Depression in the early 1930s, the yard did not finally close until 1948, making it one of the longest surviving shipbuilding bases on the Tyne.

Over a period of 95 years the Low Walker Yard built 351 screw steamers (mainly cargo ships), 145 oil tankers, 76 passenger vessels, six icebreakers, seven train ferries (some with an icebreaking capability), four suction dredgers, six steam yachts, 21 gunboats, 11 cruisers, two coast defence battleships, three customs cruisers and five sailing ships. Numerous paddle steamers and barges were also launched.

These ships were produced for many nations. The list includes Britain, Russia, Turkey, Germany, Australia, France, Italy, Egypt, India, Norway, Holland, China, Japan, Brazil, Belgium, Spain, Canada, Romania and Chile.

Ships which went from Walker to the world helped Charles Mitchell make profits which paid for the building of a hospital and Mechanics Institute and Hall at Walker and for the building and decoration of St George's Church at Jesmond, including provision of an organ.

The landmark bell-tower of St George's, similar to the campanile of St Mark's in Venice, can be seen from many parts of Newcastle. The church, completed in 1888, is the direct result of the often hard and dangerous work carried out by the men of the Low Walker Yard and of the talents and generosity of Charles Mitchell.

The industrious shipbuilder was also a benefactor of the university in his native city. Money from his fortune paid for the building of Aberdeen University's Graduation Hall, known as Mitchell Hall, complete with impressive stained glass windows, the Students' Union building, and the heightening of the university's Marischal College tower, which was renamed the Mitchell Tower in his honour. In addition, his money paid for the tower's clock and bell.

As a young man, the shipbuilder had been a part-time student of chemistry at Marischal College. He had clearly not forgotten his native city or the learning he gained there.

In February 1893, Aberdeen University bestowed an honorary degree upon Charles in recognition of his generosity. The new buildings were officially opened in October 1895, only two months after his death.

The hard-working shipbuilder passed away at Jesmond Towers on August 22, 1895. He was aged 76. Appropriately, the funeral service was held at St George's, the beautiful church Charles Mitchell had paid for. Equally appropriately, among those attending the funeral were around 600 workmen from the Low Walker and Elswick yards.

St George's Church, and, in the distance, Jesmond Towers, around 1888.

Disaster on the Slipway

Frequent accidents in the shipyards of the Tyne, including his own, turned Charles' mind to the importance of providing prompt medical attention for injured workmen. Accordingly, he paid for the construction of the Walker Infirmary, a cottage hospital which could treat the casualties. The cost was £2,000. The infirmary became known as the Walker Accident Hospital and later as the Walker Park Hospital.

This important medical facility was officially opened in May 1870 by the Mayor of Newcastle, James Morrison, in the presence of members of his council and the local board of health.

In those days the hospital had 16 beds, which could be increased to 20 in an emergency. Its first surgeon was Dr James R. Lowndes who gave his services free of charge. The first matron was a Miss Raynes.

Charles was present at the opening ceremony and he told the gathering that it was proposed that each workman in Walker contribute a penny ha'penny per week towards the maintenance of the hospital.

The first patient was Patrick Butler who had suffered a fractured leg when he fell from staging (scaffolding) placed against the side of a ship in one of the yards.

But it was not long before the new hospital had to deal with a major tragedy. In October 1870 six men were killed at the Low Walker Yard as they worked on riveting the keel of the French steamer *Transit*. The ship had moved about three feet down the slipway, crushing the men beneath.

Some of the blocks holding the vessel in position had slipped from beneath the ship and the hull began to slide towards the river. The slippage was gradual and without noise.

Several people outside the yard heard the 'piteous cries for help' of the men trapped beneath the ship and raised the alarm. John Crozier, the head foreman of the yard, lost no time in organising a band of willing workers to bring out the unfortunate men from under the vessel.

The injured and dying men were then carried to the new hospital where they were received by Dr Lowndes and his assistant, a Mr Wilson.

The men who died as a result of the accident were:

Thomas Ferries, aged 28, a riveter, single, of Walker, who had suffered head injuries. He died in the hospital with his mother at his bedside. The newspaper reported that 'this unfortunate woman has within the past few weeks lost her husband and son, both of whom met violent deaths at the same yard'.

John Yeoman, age variously given as 45 and 52, a foreman carpenter, married with a grown-up family. He received a fracture of the thigh and contusion of the abdomen. He too died in the new infirmary.

William Johnson, aged 28, riveter, single, of Earsdon, but lodging in Victoria Street, Walker. His injuries were so severe that he died while being taken to the infirmary.

Michael Adams, aged 35, a riveter, married with three children between three and five years told, of Gibson Street, Newcastle. He also died on the way to hospital.

James Kelly, aged 26, a riveter, single, of Byker Street, Walker. He was found crushed to death beneath the vessel.

Joseph Newark, aged 25, a riveter, married with one child aged two, of High Friar Street, Newcastle. This unfortunate man was identified by his clothing.

At least one worker in the vicinity lived to tell the tale. A boy employed in carrying the heated rivets escaped unhurt. A tin can from which he had been drinking was completely flattened.

The Walker Accident Hospital, opened in 1870.

An inquest into the tragedy reached the conclusion that 'the ship moved and sank owing to want of sufficient support by bilge blocks and other shores, and, further, sufficient care had not been exercised by the managers and foreman in charge of the ship'.

Clearly, the little hospital at Walker was, as Charles Mitchell had realised, a much needed facility. Fatal accidents continued to occur. For example, in June 1890 an inquest was held at the Walker Mechanics' Institute into the death of Thomas Ivory, a plater who was secretary of the local lodge of the Boilermakers' Society. He had died at the hospital on June 13 from injuries received the day before as a result of a fall at the Low Walker Yard. Thomas Ivory left a wife and three children.

Mr J.R.D. Lynn, Coroner for South Northumberland, commented 'that many a time he had been struck with the carelessness that existed during the construction of ships, and there seemed to be more carelessness with regard to life and limb in that trade than in any other manufacture he knew of, and he supposed it was chiefly owing to the men's eagerness to get on with work and make as much money as possible'.

After this accident an Ambulance Corps was formed by volunteers at the yard to administer first aid.

Two years later, in August 1892, there was another inquest into a death at the shipyard. The tragic worker was John Potter, aged 30, of St Peter's, Newcastle. It was reported that John Ward, a shipwright, had seen the man fall from the vessel to the ground.

His impression was that John Potter had caught his foot against a nut, slipped and had fallen over the ship's side. Catherine Holmes, a nurse at the Walker Hospital, said that the man had died from a fractured skull.

In November 1897 John Rutherford, a plater's helper, was assisting with the fixing of a plate on the side of a vessel when the plate gave a sudden jerk, knocking the unfortunate man off the staging to the ground about 30ft below. He was given first aid by the yard Ambulance Corps and taken to the hospital.

A particularly sad and heart-rending accident occurred in May 1902 when a 14-year-old boy was killed. He also fell to his death from staging. The inquest was held at the Stack Hotel, Walker. John Dodds, of Church Street, Walker, identified the body as that of his son, Matthew.

The boy was working as a rivet heater and fell from the main deck of a vessel on to some staging five feet below. Tragically, he rebounded off this structure and fell again, this time plummeting some 20ft to the bottom of the ship. Matthew died before the men could carry him from the vessel.

Returning a verdict of accidental death, the inquest jurors 'were of the opinion that the employment of three young boys was too hazardous and that the age should be increased from the present age of 14'. Once again, shipbuilding had proved to be a highly dangerous occupation.

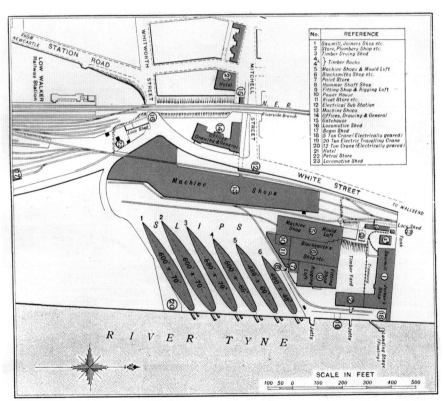

A map of the Low Walker Shipyard. (From 'The Shipyards of Armstrong Whitworth', 1921.)

Trouble and Strife

Like the other shipyards on the Tyne, Mitchell's at Low Walker had its fair share of strikes and industrial disputes. One of the most unusual of these occurred in July 1869 when two Irish labourers refused to work overtime. The reaction of their foreman or 'gaffer' to this decision sparked a strike.

A large number of Irishmen were employed to carry iron plates for the ships to the platers. The trouble began after several of the platers were requested to work overtime. One of them, a man named Sheely, spoke to two of the labourers and asked them if they would put in the extra hours. The labourers refused, saying they lived in South Shields and if they worked overtime this would cause them great inconvenience and expense since they would miss the ferry down river.

Mr Sheely, no doubt finding himself in a difficult position, did the only thing he could and told the foreman of the yard, Mr Coulson, about the situation and asked for two other assistants. Coulson, an Englishman, then inquired why the men would not work overtime and Sheely replied that they lived a considerable distance away from the works and would miss their passage on the boat home.

Mr Coulson then asked the plater for the names of the two labourers but Mr Sheely said he was unable to give the

Low Walker Shipyard, 1868. (From 'The Shipyards of Armstrong Whitworth', 1921.)

information. The foreman inquired if they were Irishmen and was told they were. Coulson was said to have replied: 'If they are two Irishmen and will not oblige me by going on tonight, they need not come in tomorrow.'

Mr Sheely reported these remarks to the two labourers who considered that their gaffer had used the term 'Irishmen' in an offensive way. News of the remarks spread to the other Irish workers, sparking anger and discontent. Within a few days 160 of them were on strike, calling for the dismissal of the foreman.

The company accused the men of breaking the rules under which they were engaged. These rules had been read to them before they were taken on and included the requirement to give a fortnight's notice if they wished to leave. The men did not dispute this, but replied that three days before the strike the foreman had dismissed two Irishmen without giving them notice and if the masters could break the rules with impunity why should the rules be binding upon the men?

The Irishmen said they were satisfied with their wages and hours. Their only complaint was the insult from the gaffer and the fact that two of them had been dismissed without proper notice.

Summonses were served on 13 of the men for leaving their employers without giving the required notice. The strikers then sent a deputation to Charles Mitchell, in the hope of reaching a peaceful solution to the dispute. Charles was told of the foreman's words and he said that if the men would return to work and pay the costs incurred up to that time, the summonses would be withdrawn. But the men refused to accept this offer and remained on strike.

The unlucky 13 labourers therefore duly appeared before Newcastle magistrates at the Moot Hall Police Court. By this time they had told a solicitor they would return to work if the prosecution was withdrawn. The solicitor, a Mr Joel, told the Bench that the men wished to go back.

He had to promise, on behalf of the men, that if they wished to leave after this misunderstanding they would give the required 14 days' notice. It appeared to him that the proper course to take, as he had advised his clients, was to lay their grievances before their employers and not all leave together without giving notice.

Mr W.S. Daglish, prosecuting, told the court he had no wish to press the case with severity against any of the men. His remarks were at variance with the men's earlier account of the matter. Mr Daglish contended that Charles Mitchell and Co. had always strictly observed the rules on their side and 'though it might often be to their advantage to be able to dismiss some of their workmen without notice, they had never yet done so.'

Both sides had rattled their sabres at one another, but the heat was rapidly disappearing from the argument. With the promise of the men to return to work the dispute was over and the magistrates took no action against them.

Many other disputes, of course, concerned pay and hours of work. In early 1904, for example, a scarcity of orders resulted in three-quarter-time working for the men at Low Walker. This enabled the company to employ a greater number of workers, but the short-time arrangement was unpopular, since it naturally led to loss of wages. The men claimed the firm had more work in hand than any other yard on the North East Coast on short-time.

The men understood that full-time working would be resumed on February 1, 1904, but when they reached the yard that morning they were told they were still on three-quarter time. The workers then held a meeting outside the gates and decided they would not return to their employment unless the management agreed to reinstate full-time hours. Mitchell's refused to see a deputation to discuss the situation 'owing to the irregularity of the proceedings'.

Punitive action was not slow in coming. The company imposed a week's lock-out on the men who had attended the meeting. At the same time, however, Mitchell's told them that after the lock-out had ended they could go back to full-time. It was a mixture of retaliation and concession. No doubt the lock-out reduced the wages bill for a week. But the craftsmen and labourers were warned that full-time working would mean the employment of fewer men. This appears to have been accepted without major protest.

If a man's job on a ship came to an end and there was no other work, he and his fellow workmen would be laid off until their services were needed again. In such circumstances they would go in search of employment at another yard and, if they were lucky, find it. Men were helped in their search for jobs by the existence, from 1862 to 1908, of a ferry boat service up and down the river between Newcastle and North and South Shields. Owned by the Tyne General Ferry Company, the

The paddle ferry Audrey passes the North Pier lighthouse at the mouth of the Tyne on her return from a pleasure trip. The Audrey and her sister the Aileen, were both built at Low Walker for the Tyne General Ferry Company. They were launched in 1897.

paddle steamers which ran on this route connected the various shipyards both north and south of the river.

Steamers left Newcastle Quayside at regular intervals throughout the day, calling at the mouth of the Ouseburn, St Peter's, High Felling, Bill Quay, High Walker, Low Walker, Hebburn, Carville (Wallsend), Hebburn Colliery, Howdon, Jarrow, Howdon Dock, Tyne Dock, Mill Dam, North Shields Landing and North Shields Fish Quay. In the summer, the service was extended to the North and South Piers at the mouth of the Tyne for those enjoying their leisure time. There were also pleasure excursions to the coastal waters of Northumberland.

By the time the Tyne General Ferry Company's services ended in 1908 it owned a fleet of 16 boats and, in its final year, carried five million passengers. About half this figure represented workmen travelling to and from the shipyards each day.

The ferry company provided the Low Walker Yard with orders. The yard built three of its paddle steamers, the *Phoebe*, launched in 1895, and the *Audrey* and *Aileen*, both dating from 1897.

The steel-hulled *Phoebe* slid down the ways into the Tyne on March 14, 1895. Her paddle engines were fitted by the Wallsend Slipway & Engineering Company, of which Charles Mitchell was first chairman. The vessel was named *Phoebe* by Miss Rea, daughter of Mr J. Rea, secretary of the owners.

The 126ft-long *Audrey* was launched at Low Walker on May 2, 1897. She was built very much with the comfort of passengers in mind. The boat was designed for sea excursions as well as river service; and she featured a refreshment bar, tea buffet, and toilets of a 'good' standard. The *Audrey* could carry up to 600 passengers on the river service and about 250 at sea, so that she could go on summer excursions to the Farne Islands and other places of interest along the North East coast. At the launch the steamer was named *Audrey* by Mrs Rogerson, the wife of Mr J.E. Rogerson, a director of the Tyne General Ferry Company.

A. Reid and Co., Ltd., Newcastle.

O. Rosenvinge.

VIEW ON TYNE.

TYNE GENERAL FERRY COMPANY.

HALF-HOUR SAILINGS FROM QUAYSIDE, NEWCASTLE } TYNEMOUTH FARES: 6D. SINGLE. SHIELDS FARES: 4D SINGLE.
" " 9D. RETURN.. " " 6D. RETURN.

"No English river is at all comparable to the Tyne in the evidences which it everywhere thrusts forward of the part which it plays in the industrial development of these Islands."—W. E. GLADSTONE.

The last of the trio from Low Walker, the *Aileen,* entered the Tyne on June 17, 1897. A sister to the *Audrey*, she was also to be used for passenger excursions as well as the day-to-day river ferry service. The christening ceremony was performed by Kitty Swan, daughter of Charles Mitchell's partner, Henry F. Swan.

It is intriguing to think that some of the Low Walker workers who built these boats would have gone on to use regularly them for travelling up and down river and even, perhaps, for summer excursions to the North Sea.

Steam Yachts and Millionaires

Steam yachts were elegant and often luxurious examples of the shipbuilder's art. Constructed for the private use of wealthy customers, they were essentially the pleasure boats of millionaires, aristocrats and princes. Charles Mitchell's Low Walker Yard built several of these vessels during its early years, the first, as we have seen, being the *George Robert* of 1856.

Ten years later, in 1866, another steam yacht was completed at Low Walker, the *Northumbria,* built for George Robert Stephenson, then head of the renowned firm of Robert Stephenson & Co, of Newcastle, which had pioneered the building of early steam locomotives and also constructed other types of engine. In fact, Stephenson's provided the reciprocating engines for the vessel and these drove a four-bladed propeller. In addition, the *Northumbria* carried sails on three masts.

A contemporary account describes the yacht as 'rakish looking, moulded on the finest lines' and she featured a figurehead, described as a beautiful female figure holding a miner's pick in one hand and a lump of coal in the other. These were, of course, very appropriate emblems for a Tyne-built vessel.

Her crew of 13 seamen were 'picked men from Cowes' dressed in blue uniforms with white facings and gilt buttons adorned with an anchor. The front of their caps carried the word *Northumbria* in gilt letters.

It was reported at the time of her launch that George Robert Stephenson's motive in ordering this beautiful yacht was not merely pleasure and healthy recreation. The main reason, it was stated, was to demonstrate to southern yacht owners that the Tyne could produce fine examples of this type of vessel equal to those constructed in other parts of Britain.

The steam yacht was launched into the Tyne by Miss Isabella Stephenson, the eldest daughter of the owner, who broke a bottle of champagne over the yacht's bows in traditional fashion, christening her the *Northumbria*. The owner's daughters wore dresses which echoed those of the seamen – they were white and trimmed with blue and gilt buttons.

The weather was cool owing to an easterly wind but seemed to have no effect on the enjoyment of the event by spectators. Not surprisingly, those present included the wealthy Mr Stephenson, nephew of famed railway locomotive pioneer George Stephenson. Keeping a close eye on the proceedings to see that all went smoothly was Henry F. Swan, by then a managing partner at the yard.

The Stephenson works band played the *Keel Row* as the yacht began to move down the ways, followed by *Rule Britannia* after she was afloat. Once the ceremony was over the official guests were treated to lunch in the draughting loft. This meal was supplied by a Mr Jeffries of the Central Station Hotel in Newcastle.

The *Northumbria* had been designed by William Dobson, Mitchell's foreman shipwright, who was presented with a gold watch by Stephenson. A silver watch was presented to a Mr McLauchlan for his fine joinery work.

Stephenson was clearly delighted with his new steam yacht for he provided £150 to pay for dinner for the workmen employed at the yard, with the provision that the meal take place during Newcastle's Race Week.

The men were given a week's paid holiday, and to add to the festivities, they attended the launching at Low Walker of a 'powerful and beautiful' paddle steamer for the Russian Steam Navigation Company and intended for Black Sea service. A large crowd went to the riverside to watch the vessel slide into the water, which she did in 'splendid' style. The ship was named the *General Kotzebue*.

After the launch, the workmen assembled at the gates of the yard where a procession was formed, headed by the band of the 8th Northumberland Volunteers of Walker. The banners belonging to the boilermakers were carried in the procession which paraded through parts of Newcastle before they all went to dinner.

About 800 men were given the meal, including senior staff members of Mitchell's and Stephenson's along with officials of the Russian Steam Navigation Co. This was provided at several public houses and hotels in the Newcastle area.

A newspaper account reported that after the meal 'a number of songs were sung and proceedings were of a most hilarious and pleasant character'. Clearly, it seems a good time was had by all. The event illustrates the high value of the pound in 1866 – a meal for 800 people had been provided at a cost of £150!

The *Northumbria* was not the last steam yacht to be launched at the Low Walker Yard. Two examples of this type of vessel, both named the *Nora*, came from its slipways. The first *Nora*, like the second, was built for Mons. Jean Baptiste Perret, a wealthy French senator of Lyons, but she was wrecked off St Mary's Island, Whitley Bay, on April 24, 1879, while undergoing trials. On board for this trial trip were representatives of the shipbuilders, engine builders and owner. They included Henry F. Swan and William Dobson, who had risen to become yard manager and who would eventually set up his own shipyard at Walker.

The steam yacht had just completed a satisfactory run on the measured mile and was being turned around to steam back to the Tyne when she hit the wreck of the steamer *Longhirst,* a short distance to the north of St Mary's Island. There was no buoy marking the wreck. The bottom of the yacht's hull was torn open and she began sinking fast. The *Nora* went down by the head, her propeller lifting out of the water as she did so.

The 44 crew and passengers on board had only a short time to get into the boats, but fortunately these were ready for launching. A young man was in the propeller tunnel oiling the machinery when the accident happened and he had great difficulty escaping as the engine room began filling with water. Luckily, however, he managed to reach the open deck and survived along with everyone else.

One of the survivors had to keep his thumb in the plug hole of a lifeboat to prevent it sinking until a plug could be found. There was a heavy swell hitting the shore of the island but the boats managed to find a safe place to land. It had been a narrow escape.

Elegant princess. The Low Walker steam yacht Nora passes down the Tyne. This vessel, launched in December 1879, was the second Nora, being a replacement for a steam yacht of the same name wrecked off St Mary's Island, Whitley Bay, in April 1879.

In December 1879 a second *Nora* was launched at Low Walker to replace her wrecked predecessor. Both vessels had been named after Mons. Perret's Irish wife. The second yacht was larger than the first. She was 170ft long and featured a clipper bow with a female figurehead and, as was usually the case, an elaborately carved stern. Her engines were supplied by R. & W. Hawthorn, of Newcastle. Her cabin accommodation was described as 'sumptuous' with room for eight guests. There was an owner's suite, lounge, music room and dining room. Upholstery and decorations were French in style.

Among other steam yachts from Low Walker was the *Cumbria*, built in 1881 for the Earl of Lonsdale, of Lowther Castle, Westmorland. The *Cumbria* was certainly a most remarkable yacht, constructed and fitted out regardless of expense. A shapely clipper bow was crowned by a figurehead

The barque-rigged steam yacht Cumbria, built at Low Walker in 1881 for the Earl of Lonsdale, of Lowther Castle, Westmorland. Here, the Cumbria is lying in the Tyne.

of a dragon rampant, and the stern was decorated with carved woodwork. Accommodation for the owner and his guests was described as 'beautiful' and there was even a doctor's room on board.

The vessel carried four two-and-a-quarter-inch guns, although it is not recorded why such warlike fittings were considered necessary. Her steam compound surface condensing engines were supplied by the Wallsend Slipway and Engineering Co. Ltd., giving her a speed of 11 knots. The vessel also carried a fine array of square sails.

She was indeed impressive, but Lord Lonsdale did not live long to enjoy his wonderful steam yacht. He died suddenly in 1882, only a year after the *Cumbria* was delivered.

Tugs for Siberia

The Low Walker Yard built over 90 vessels of various types for Russian owners, including icebreakers. The first of the Russian ships was a steamer, the *Possochoff*, of 1856. The river paddle steamers *Krikoon, Kronstadt, Volga* and *Kama* followed in 1858.

The next year saw the completion of the paddle tugs *Karacheff, Looga, Luban* and *Neva* for service on the River Volga, as well as the paddle steamers *Olga, Goloubchick*, and *Caucusus.*

Around 1862 Charles, together with his business partner Henry F. Swan, began the work of setting up an iron shipbuilding yard for the Tsarist government in St Petersburg. The Russians had made the decision to switch from wooden to iron construction. Several warships were built there under the guidance of the partners, with members of their staff providing crucial training. Henry F. Swan went out to St Petersburg to direct operations, taking over from Charles who had gone there to start off the venture.

The first ships to be built at the Russian yard under the contract with Mitchell's were the coastal defence vessels *Smertch* (Waterspout) and *Netron Menya* (Touch Me Not) in 1865. The last was the *Kniaz Pojarski,* launched in 1867 but not completed until 1873.

In recognition of his services, Russia made Charles Mitchell a Cavalier of the Order of St Stanislaus, a rare honour for a Briton. In addition, Tsar Alexander II presented both Charles and Henry with ornamental snuff boxes inlaid with diamonds.

The Russian High Admiral, the Grand Duke Constantine, visited Newcastle as a guest of Charles in 1871. The High Admiral and other senior ranking Russian naval officers were entertained to dinner at Jesmond Towers and the next day were taken on a tour of the Low Walker Yard.

Business with Russia continued. In the summer of 1894 two powerful paddle tugs, the *Pervoi* and *Vtori*, were completed at Low Walker. They were designed for towing service on the River Yenesei and its tributaries in the middle of Siberia with the object of delivering materials for the Trans-Siberian Railway.

The currents of some of these rivers are extremely rapid and, in addition to paddle machinery, the tugs were also fitted with large hauling engines, which were designed so that each tug could haul herself and barges up the rapids by means of a chain which was laid into the river bed. The vessels were also equipped with powerful gearing on deck and separate engines to work the gearing. Before being delivered to Russia, chains were laid in the Tyne to test this ingenious equipment.

The main engines were in duplicate and arranged so that the two paddle wheels on each vessel could be worked independently of each other, and even in opposite directions for the greater convenience in handling. These engines were of 600 horsepower and the boilers were constructed for burning wood as fuel.

Novel and powerful these steamers certainly were, but the task of delivering them from the Tyne to Siberia was a tricky one. The River Yenesei flows northwards across Siberia into the Arctic waters of the Kara Sea, which are icebound for much of the year. The delivery voyage thus required a captain who knew the route around the North Cape of Norway and through the seas of the Russian Arctic.

Such a seaman was Captain Joseph Wiggins, the former Board of Trade examiner in seamanship for the Sunderland and South Shields areas. Born in Norfolk, he had served in sailing ships of the North East Coast and had married a Sunderland girl. Wiggins had helped to open up a trading route into the Kara Sea, giving access to the mouths of the Ob and Yenesei rivers and enabling ships to bring back timber, furs and other cargoes from Siberia.

Accordingly, on August 8, 1894, a small flotilla of ships left the Tyne bound for the Russian Arctic and under the overall command of Captain Wiggins. It consisted of the Low Walker tugs *Pervoi* and *Vtori* and the Arctic yacht *Blencathra*, owned by Hugh Popham, a well-known yachtsman. At a port on the Norwegian coast they were met by the wooden steamer *Stjernen*, which it was planned would return the crews of the vessels to Britain.

All went well with the outward voyage and Wiggins successfully delivered the Tyne-built tugs to the Russian authorities at a place called Lokovoi Protok some 500 miles up the Yenisei. He and the delivery crews left there on September 15 of that year in a voyage home on the *Stjernen*. Then they

Captain Wiggins (from 'The Life and Voyages of Joseph Wiggins' by Henry Johnson, 1907).

disappeared for nearly four months before details of their escape from shipwreck became known to the outside world.

They had reached the Kara Sea safely but later the *Stjernen* had hit a reef off the coast of the Yamal Peninsula during dense fog. This fog persisted and the wind became stronger. The damaged ship settled broadside on to the rocks in a heavy swell. The situation was now so serious that Wiggins gave the order to abandon ship and with difficulty the crews were safely landed on the barren shores of the Yamal Peninsula, home to the Samoyed people of northern Siberia. Hugh Popham and three other men volunteered to walk to the settlement of Chabrova to enlist the help of the Samoyeds.

Eventually they reached the tent of a Russian trader named Ivan Koshevin and he set out for the place where the survivors were encamped, accompanied by a group of Samoyeds on

The Russian paddle tugs Pervoi and Vtori lying in the Tyne before their departure for the River Yenesei, Siberia.

sledges. Eventually more sledges, pulled by reindeer, arrived to help the seamen as news of their landing spread and most of the provisions aboard the wreck were recovered. It was necessary to take food and other stores from the ship because food was in short supply in Chabrova.

Ivan Koshevin and the Samoyeds showed great kindness to

the seamen and it was due to their help that they survived the immense journey that lay ahead of them. Fur suits and other outfits made from reindeer skins were provided for the men and the Samoyeds also gave them their spare tents for shelter at night.

Captain Wiggins and his men travelled for 32 days for between 500 and 600 miles across the frozen tundra accompanied and guided by the Samoyeds and 2,000 head of reindeer. By November 17 all the party of 49 men had reached Pustozersk on the Petchora River. Two men were suffering badly from frostbite and one had to have two or three of his toes amputated.

On December 15, 1894, the crews reached the port of Archangel without major mishap, although five men who had been taken ill were admitted to hospital on arrival. The party learned that two vessels had been sent out, one from Norway and one from the Yenisei, in search of them.

The wreck of the Stjernen (from 'The Life and Voyages of Joseph Wiggins' by Henry Johnson, 1907).

Their fate had naturally been the subject of much speculation.

Captain Wiggins later said that the loss of the *Stjernen* was a sea accident which might have happened anywhere in the world and did not in any way discredit the navigability of the sea route to Siberia.

The tugs *Pervoi* and *Vtori* were not the only connections between the Low Walker Yard and the Kara Sea route. Between the First and Second World Wars the Russian icebreaker *Lenin* was often on duty in the Yugorski Strait leading into the southern part of the sea to clear or guide the way for ships heading for the mouths of the Yenisei and the Ob. The *Lenin* had been completed at Low Walker under the name *St Alexander Nevski* in 1917.

Russian Icebreakers

By the early 1900s the Low Walker Yard had gained a fine reputation for the construction of icebreakers and was at the forefront of their design. Russia proved to be a major customer for these highly specialised vessels.

As early as 1856 a Mitchell-built ship had made news when she tackled ice on a river. The vessel was the *Pollux*, which went through ice up to five feet thick on an experimental passage up the River Elbe in Germany.

Built for a Hamburg firm, the *Pollux*, a screw steamer, had been launched at Low Walker the previous year. However, she was not specifically built as an icebreaker. Her voyage up river was a test to see the extent to which it was possible to keep navigation open during the winter months. The vessel was trimmed by the stern so that her bow would rise up to crush the ice.

Eight years later, in 1862, Mitchell's completed the *Pilot*, a tug which was to become one of the first true icebreakers. Again, she was not specifically built as such. Constructed for a Russian owner named Britnev, the *Pilot* was used in the waters of the Kronstadt and St Petersburg areas. Around 1870 Britnev had a new, stronger bow built on the vessel so that she could keep a passage open through the ice longer than was usually possible between Kronstadt and St Petersburg. She was

The steamer Pollux tackles the ice on the River Elbe in 1856 (Illustrated London News, 2 February 1856).

also used to keep the canal open between Kronstadt and Oranienbaum, then a railway terminus on the coast.

Mitchell's took an important step forward in 1895 when the Low Walker Yard launched its first purpose-built icebreaker, the *Saratovski Ledokol*, for service on the River Volga. Her job was to keep a passage open through the ice for a train ferry, the *Saratovskaia Pereprava*, which was also built at the yard.

The icebreaker was transported on barges in two longitudinal sections through the Marinski Canal system to the Volga crossing point of the Riazan-Ouralsk Railway. The ship had to be divided in this way since it was too wide to pass through the canal locks. Similarly,

The Saratovski Ledokol breaks the ice on the River Volga. She had been launched at the yard in 1895.

the train ferry was divided, this time into four sections, both longitudinally and transversely, for the passage through the canals. It was an ingenious feat of design and technology.

Reporting on the launch of the *Saratovski Ledokol*, in May 1895, the *Newcastle Daily Journal* said that she was 'probably the most powerful icebreaker in the world which is intended to be employed in conjunction with a large railway ferry steamer, also building at the same yard, in carrying railway trucks across the River Volga. As it is desired to carry the service

throughout the winter, when the ice of the river is of great thickness, it became necessary to provide a very powerful icebreaker.'

The vessel was 150ft long with a 26ft beam and fitted with twin screw engines of 1,400hp. A considerable amount of the shell plating was an inch thick, giving it great strength.

The train ferry *Saratovskaia Pereprava* was launched a month after the icebreaker. She was intended to carry railway trains across a swift flowing river, the level of which varied by

40ft. For loading and discharging the railway trucks, a special hydraulic hoist was constructed at the Elswick Works and fitted into the bow of the vessel. The hoist was arranged so that the trucks could be run on and off the ship whatever the level of the river.

By early August the train ferry was undergoing trials up and down the Tyne and many people were curious about her intended purpose.

The delivery of these two cleverly constructed vessels was an achievement of great magnitude for the company, but in 1895-98 the Low Walker Yard carried out an even more ambitious project – the delivery of an icebreaking train ferry to the shores of Lake Baikal in the middle of Siberia. The ship, appropriately named the *Baikal,* was designed to carry passengers, carriages and trucks across the lake between two sections of the Trans-Siberian Railway.

At that date, a line around the southern shores of this huge expanse of water was still in the planning stage and was not constructed until 1900-1904. Those building this track were faced with rocky and mountainous terrain and this necessitated tunnelling and the building of bridges in sometimes harsh weather conditions.

Before the line came into service, passengers and freight had therefore to travel across the deep waters of Lake Baikal between Baranchuk on the northern shore to Mysovaya on the southern.

The train ferry *Baikal* was constructed on a slipway at Low Walker, taking under a year to complete. She was then dismantled and the different sections and pieces were marked and shipped from the Tyne to St Petersburg. From there, the parts, which weighed almost 3,000 tons in total, were

The icebreaking train ferry Baikal under construction on the shores of Lake Baikal, Siberia.

The impressive-looking icebreaking train ferry Baikal. Her facilities included a chapel, which became a favourite wedding venue.

transported in about 6,900 packages by rail and river to Irkutsk, the largest town near the western side of the lake. It was reported that the items were then carried by pony-drawn sledges to the lake.

The first consignment of sections had left Low Walker in 1896 and only in late 1898 did the last consignment reach its destination, the village of Listvennitchnaya on the lake shore. The ship was then put together again and launched.

The task of reconstructing the *Baikal* was led by a team of engineers from Tyneside, whose journey to Siberia must have been something of an adventure. In charge of the team was Andrew Douie. His assistants were a Mr Renton, an aptly-named Mr Handy and a fourth man.

They lived in the small village of Listvennitchnaya, where robbery and other crimes were said to be commonplace. Few went out after dark and many people carried revolvers for protection.

It was reported that a considerable number of the men

working on the rebuilding of the *Baikal*, including the foreman of the labourers, had been transported to Siberia for alleged crimes. One man working on the ship was wanted for allegedly killing eight people.

The *Baikal* was launched into the lake in June 1899 and was then towed to Baranchuk for fitting out. By January 1900 she was undergoing trials, successfully tackling ice between 18 inches and four feet thick. In the summer of that year she at last entered service on her intended route. The project had taken over four years to complete.

The 290ft-long *Baikal* was of 5,280 gross tons and had cabins for 150 passengers. The ship even had her own restaurant. She also featured a chapel, which became a popular place for Siberian couples to hold their weddings.

Her two propulsion engines were of 3,750 horsepower, driving twin propellers. A third engine drove another propeller positioned under the vessel's bow, which was designed to cause the ice above to lose much of its natural support so that it would crack more easily as it was crushed by the ship's advancing bows. The four-funnel vessel was adapted to burn wood as fuel. Her steel hull was one-inch thick and backed by nearly two feet of timber.

She carried three lines on her rail deck which were capable of accommodating goods trucks or passenger carriages. The centre track could be used by the large sleeping cars of the Trans-Siberian Railway.

Meanwhile, parts for a passenger-carrying icebreaker, to be named *Angara*, had also been arriving at the lake. This ship, too, was constructed at the Low Walker Yard, dismantled and shipped out to St Petersburg, thence travelling by rail to the lake shore.

The two-funnel *Angara* was then reassembled, launched and began service in late 1900. However, the train ferry was the more powerful vessel and often helped to clear the way through the ice for the *Angara* when conditions were particularly severe. The two ships carried thousands of the Tsar's troops eastwards to the Russo-Japanese War of 1904-05.

The *Baikal* was destroyed in the early 1920s during the Russian Civil War which followed the Revolution of 1917. The *Angara* gained notoriety by becoming the scene of a brutal massacre in the same conflict. In early 1920 forces allied to the

The Russian icebreaker Angara cuts through the frozen waters of Lake Baikal, Siberia. She became the scene of a notorious massacre during the Russian Civil War.

White Russian armies seized 31 Menshevik socialists and Social Revolutionaries. They were taken aboard the ship and clubbed to death with a mallet as the vessel steamed over the lake. Their bodies were then tossed into the icy waters.

The *Angara* atrocity angered the people of the Irkutsk area and the unsavoury episode was instrumental in the downfall of Admiral Kolchak, leader of the Whites in Siberia. Even though the forces which carried out the killing were not directly under his control, Kolchak's reputation was tainted by his association with them.

The passenger icebreaker *Angara* survives today on the River Angara, Irkutsk where she has been converted to a floating museum.

In 1899 another icebreaker had been launched at Low Walker. She was the *Ledokoll III*, which had been ordered by the port authorities of Odessa on the Black Sea. The 150ft-long vessel was adequate for work in ice about three feet thick.

However, Russia was not the only country that placed orders for icebreakers with the yard. In April 1898 the *Sampo* was launched for Finland. Her main task was to keep the port of Hango open during the winter and also to carry out similar work in Helsinki. Another Finnish icebreaker, the *Tarmo*, was launched by the company in 1907.

In addition, Low Walker built three icebreaking train ferries for service in Canada. The first, the *Scotia*, was built for service across the Strait of Canso, separating Cape Breton Island from the mainland of Nova Scotia. Completed in 1901, she was an odd looking vessel. Her four funnels were situated on the extreme sides of the ship.

Many years later the *Armstrong Whitworth Record* commented: 'The navigation bridge is carried on a series of

Scotia at sea.

braced gantries and combines with the funnels to produce a very un-nautical effect.' A story was told that when the *Scotia* was running her trials off the North East coast an onlooker at Hartley, near Blyth, said to a friend, 'Whey, Geordie, there's Bedlington Colliery gannin awa' to sea.'

The two other train ferries for Canada were the 300ft-long *Prince Edward Island*, of 2,795 gross tons, which was launched in 1914, and the *Scotia II*, of 1,859 gross tons, which entered the Tyne the following year.

The appropriately named *Prince Edward Island* was built for service between Prince Edward Island near the Gulf of St Lawrence and the Canadian mainland. The *Scotia II* succeeded the earlier vessel on the Strait of Canso route.

The need for ships to move through icebound seas had kept many men in work at Low Walker.

Tackling the Frozen Seas

Perhaps the most impressive of the Low Walker icebreakers was the *Yermak*, built for the Russian government for service in the Baltic, Gulf of Finland and Arctic seas. She is generally regarded as the first icebreaker designed for polar use.

With a displacement of nearly 8,000 tons, the *Yermack* (often referred to as the *Ermack*) was one of the larger ships of her type to be constructed at the yard. The 305ft-long vessel was launched in October 1898.

The idea of building the ship was conceived by Vice Admiral Stepan Makarov who believed that a powerful icebreaker should keep the Baltic open for Russian ships during the winter and then steam to the Russian Arctic in the spring where she could force open an early trading passage to the Kara Sea and Siberian rivers while ice still gripped that area.

At the *Yermack's* launch, Henry F. Swan told guests that Admiral Makarov, besides sketching out the broad principles of the ship, had been of the greatest help to Armstrong Whitworth in working out the technical details. Among those present was Captain Vasiliev, the man who was to take the ship through the Baltic on her delivery voyage to Kronstadt. Madame Vasiliev, the captain's wife, performed the launching ceremony.

The captain was applauded as he told the crowd that the intellect and scientific skill of man would overcome nature and overwhelm the elements. He was convinced that ice in future would be no more hindrance to navigation than fogs were at present. The launch was witnessed by a huge crowd of spectators and she glided down the ways without any problems (see launch card on page 43).

The building of the *Yermack* had presented many difficulties, but the Low Walker Yard had solved them. The hull was divided into 48 watertight compartments.

By early March 1899 the *Yermack* was undergoing her first trials off the Tyne. The ship left the river on her maiden voyage to Kronstadt on April 2, 1899. *Engineering* reported: 'Her arrival at Kronstadt was evidently an extraordinary sight. The ice was about 18 inches thick with a good deal of snow on top, and the ship steamed through this at six-and-a-half knots up to the sea wall and past the battleships. She swung around on the port hand and entered the harbour though an entrance only 95 feet wide; the ship, it will be remembered is of 71 feet beam… The outer skin is polished bright where the vessel has been running through the ice, but there are no signs of leakage anywhere.'

Engineering added: 'During the progress from Tolbeacon (Tokouchin) Light into the harbour the ship was accompanied by thousands of people on sledges, and the colonel of a regiment, who is a friend of Admiral Makarov, marched out with 60 men "on ski" to meet the vessel.'

The launch of the Russian icebreaker Yermack at Low Walker in 1898. Note the distinctive hull shape. On her delivery voyage the following year the ship cut her way through the ice of the Baltic to reach the port of Kronstadt, near St Petersburg, where she was greeted by enthusiastic Russians.

Others who made the six-mile journey across the frozen sea to meet the icebreaker included a party of Russian naval officers. The *Yermack* left behind her a wide channel in what was described as a 'desert' of ice. Some of the visitors were taken aboard and others rode alongside on sledges, but the small Finland horses had a job keeping up with the vessel. At 2pm the *Yermack* entered the port of Kronstadt where crowds of enthusiastic people cheered her as she ploughed her way through the ice to the pier.

Yermack is greeted by crowds on her arrival at Kronstadt, near St Petersburg, after her delivery voyage from the Tyne in 1899. (Picture from Le Monde Illustre, 15 April 1899.)

Russia's new icebreaker was soon proving her worth in the Gulf of Finland by rescuing numerous ships stuck in the ice. During ten days cutting channels off Tallinn, she rescued 31 ships from the frozen waters, in which some had been embedded for several weeks.

The *Yermack* featured three engines aft driving triple propellers and a fourth engine in the bow to drive an icebreaking screw. The combined horsepower of these four main engines was 10,000. A large crew and about 80 passengers and cargo could be carried. The midships section of the hull was specially formed to resist crushing and a steel belt of 25ft in height on either side of the vessel was fitted with heavy frames spaced a foot apart, supporting flush plating more than an inch thick.

Several months after her delivery the *Yermack* made an experimental voyage to Arctic waters to test her icebreaking capabilities in polar conditions. She proved herself able to break ice up to 20ft thick, but when she came up against ice of 80ft thickness her bows were severely damaged.

By late 1901 she was again back in service and Captain Vasiliev was reporting a successful Arctic voyage to Novaya Zemla and Franz Joseph Land.

In 1904, the Russian Baltic fleet left Kronstadt for its disastrous encounter with the Japanese at the Battle of Tsushima the following year. The *Yermack* helped to clear the way for these ill-fated warships as they moved out of the frozen seas for that last naval clash of the Russo-Japanese War. Tragically, Admiral Makarov lost his life in the same conflict.

Between the two World Wars the icebreaker was used in the Murmansk area and the White Sea and also did sterling service on the Kara Sea route. She survived the Second World War to again do useful work for Russia. The *Yermack* was reported to have been broken up in the mid 1960s.

During the First World War a near sister to the *Yermack* was launched at Low Walker for the Russian government. Named the *Sviatogor* (Holy Mountain), she was needed for service in the Arctic seas off Murmansk and Archangel as the

A bow view of Yermack in the ice. In 1899 she freed many ships trapped in the frozen waters of the Baltic. The impressive icebreaker is believed to have survived until the 1960s.

Baltic and Black Seas had been effectively closed to the passage of Russian and Allied ships by the conflict.

Slightly larger than the *Yermack*, the *Sviatogor* was 323ft long and when she entered service was the largest icebreaker in the world. Three engines of a combined 10,000 horsepower were fitted, driving triple propellers.

Launched in 1916, she was delivered to her base at Archangel the following year, but the outbreak of the Russian Revolution altered the course of her career. The Bolsheviks scuttled the ship in 1918 as they tried to block the port to British forces intervening in northern Russia against their revolution. However, the British raised the *Sviatogor*, repaired her and incorporated her into the Royal Navy for a few years. When the United Kingdom granted recognition to the Soviet government she was returned to Russia in late 1921.

In 1927 she was renamed the *Krasin* in a salute to L.B. Krasin, who was People's Commissar for Foreign Trade and the ship was again sent to the Arctic, being based at Murmansk. The following year she rescued members of an Italian airship expedition to the Arctic. Aircraft located the Italians' camp and the *Krasin* steamed towards their position and took them on board. In 1934 came another rescue. This time the crew of a steamer trapped in the ice were rescued.

The Second World War saw the *Krasin* helping to convoy Allied ships carrying vital supplies for the war effort. In 1957-58 she underwent major rebuilding work and emerged with new engines, a new superstructure and only one funnel instead of two. But the hull which had taken shape at the Low Walker Yard so many years before survived, a testament to the skills of her builders.

The vessel was later used as a scientific research ship and

The Russian icebreaker Sviatogor, built at Armstrong Whitworth's Low Walker Yard. Her construction was supervised by Russian naval architect Yevgeny Zamyatin, who later became a distinguished novelist.

renamed *Leonid Krasin*. For a while she also became a floating power station in the Arctic. Eventually, the name *Leonid* was dropped and she reverted to being simply the *Krasin*. Still surviving, in 1989 the *Krasin* became a museum/research ship and the following year paid a visit to London's Tilbury Docks. Sadly, a planned trip to the Tyne did not materialise.

The final icebreaker from Low Walker was the *St Alexander Nevski*, built in 1916-17 but not completed until after the Russian Revolution. Seized by the Royal Navy, she was renamed HMS *Alexander*. However, she was handed over to the Soviet government in the early 1920s and renamed *Lenin*. As we have seen, she often carried out duties on the Kara Sea route. The *Lenin* was reported to be still in service in the mid-1960s. Low Walker's icebreakers had led highly useful and sometimes long lives.

The building of the *Sviatogor* and *St Alexander Nevski* during the First World War had been supervised by Russian naval architect Yevgeny Zamyatin, who lived for over a year in Sanderson Road, Jesmond, Newcastle, while undertaking this work. His Renault motor car was probably a familiar sight at the Low Walker Yard during this period.

Zamyatin later became a distinguished author, best known for his anti-utopian novel *We*. This book is considered to have been a significant influence on George Orwell's modern classic, *1984*. The characters in *We* live in an authoritarian state where life is ordered with mechanical precision and freedom is sacrificed to ostensible happiness. People are known by numbers instead of names. Zamyatin also wrote a shorter novel, entitled *Islanders*, in which he gently satirised comfortably-off Britons, based to a great degree on his observations of the people living in Jesmond.

David Saunders, School of Historical Studies, University of Newcastle upon Tyne

Krasin at St Petersburg in 2004. She is now a museum ship, and famous because of her rescue of Italian airmen from Arctic Spitsbergen in 1928.

In all his writings he displayed a highly individual viewpoint and expressed his opinions with courageous honesty. Unsurprisingly, Zamyatin did not find favour with Stalin's regime and he left Russia for exile in Paris. *We* had no doubt been seen as a veiled criticism of the Soviet state under Stalin.

The naval architect and writer who had played a leading role in the creation of the *Sviatogor* and *St Alexander Nevski* died in 1937.

Pioneer Oil Tankers

In 1882 the Low Walker Yard completed its first oil tanker, the Russian-owned *Massis*, for service in the Caspian Sea petroleum trade. She was equipped with one tank amidships designed to carry crude petroleum but also possessed an ordinary cargo hold.

Shortly afterwards, in the same year, the yard completed two more Russian tankers for the same trade, the *Poseidon* and *Armeniak*. Of these small ships, the *Armeniak* was the more significant for future developments since she was purely an oil tanker and carried no other cargo.

Within the following 20 years Low Walker was to establish itself as one of the world's leading builders of this type of vessel. Indeed, under the guidance of Charles Mitchell's able partner, Henry F. Swan, it was a pioneer of oil tanker design.

Henry took out several patents for tank steamers and became one of the world's foremost authorities in this field. His design ideas were embodied in the *Gluckauf,* which in 1886 became the first tanker to carry oil across the Atlantic. The vessel, which was built for shipowners Riedemann of Bremen, is generally regarded as the prototype of the modern oil tanker. The *Gluckauf's* shell plating constituted an integral part of the oil tanks, which were divided into pairs by a middle line bulkhead. In each tank the oil extended to the shell and deck. Machinery was placed aft, with a short bridge amidships.

The *Gluckauf* (German: 'good luck') was launched into the Tyne on June 16, 1886, and underwent trials the following month. Shortly afterwards she departed on her maiden voyage to New York.

The makers of barrels and tin cases for oil in the United States were alarmed by the arrival of this ship whose relatively large tanks were clearly a threat to their business. They managed, for a time at least, to persuade coaling agencies to withhold supplies of bunker coal from the *Gluckauf*. However, the ship overcame this difficulty and she loaded her liquid cargo. Re-crossing the Atlantic, she reached Geestemunde towards the end of August.

Unfortunately, the career of this pioneering ship lasted less than ten years. In 1893, she ran aground on Fire Island in the approaches to New York, being declared a total loss. The wreck was sold as scrap for a mere 350 dollars.

The yard went on to build more than 140 tankers. Most of these led mundane but highly useful lives transporting oil throughout the globe. However, the carriage of such a flammable cargo has always been a potentially dangerous undertaking, and was particularly hazardous in the early years of the trade when the perils were not always fully appreciated. Low Walker's tankers were by no means immune from such accidents.

Among the ships which featured in the casualty figures was the *Ville de Calais*. Launched in August 1887 for French owners, she was fitted with triple expansion engines by the Wallsend Slipway and Engineering Company. Charles Mitchell and Henry F. Swan had been among the founders of this famous engineering concern.

In October 1888 the *Ville de Calais* arrived in the Dock Basin at Calais with a cargo of crude petroleum from America. Disaster stuck on the 16th of the month when the tanker blew up. The explosion killed four men, injured a considerable number of other people and shattered windows in

The Low Walker-built oil tanker Lux, launched in 1888. Three years later she was wrecked in the Mediterranean after catching fire.

many parts of the town, apparently causing panic amongst the residents.

The captain, his wife and another woman were aboard the vessel at the time but miraculously survived. When they emerged from their cabin in the after part of the vessel, which was the only section to remain intact, they were shocked to see that the rest of the ship, apart from a section of the forecastle, had been blown to pieces.

The explosion threw fragments of the hull and machinery a long way from the dock. One piece of iron plating fell through the roof of a house. A soldier walking about a mile from the ship received a serious leg injury from one of the fragments.

There was speculation that the blast had been caused by an engineer taking a naked light into the hold to check the ship's ballast tanks, which at the time were being pumped full of water. The flame may have ignited gas generated by the petroleum.

Only 10 people were aboard the *Ville de Calais* at the time of the blast. It is probable that loss of life would have been greater had more members of the 26-man crew been present.

During the following year an attempt by a tug to tow the stern section of the wrecked tanker to London for scrap proved a disastrous failure. Off Margate the tow rope parted and the wreck sank. John Stanford, the man who had bought the wreck of the ship, fell overboard from the tug and died of exposure.

The career of another Low Walker-built tanker, the *Lux*, also ended in tragedy. Completed in 1888 'on spec', she was sold to J.M. Lennard and Sons, of Middlesbrough. In 1889 the *Lux* arrived in the Tyne from Philadelphia with a cargo of petroleum equal to about 15,000 barrels, or a volume of 700,000 gallons. She was said at the time to be the largest tanker to bring her cargo across the Atlantic to the Tyne.

Tragedy struck in the autumn of 1891 while the ship was bound for Antwerp from Batoum with petroleum. While entering the Doro Channel near the Greek island of Negropol the *Lux* was hit by a fire which was soon out of control. Twenty people lost their lives, including Captain Brough, from Cumberland, his wife, two children and sister-in-law. There were only six survivors.

The blaze was believed to have originated in the coal bunkers and it seems likely that some of the oil she was carrying had leaked into this area and then into the stokehold bilge beneath the boilers. As the fire raged, the steamer grounded on the rocky shore of Negropol and an explosion occurred.

Accidents at sea did not always, of course, involve fire, explosion and loss of life. The Low Walker tanker *Beacon Light* struck an iceberg on her maiden voyage in May 1890. However, she managed to remain afloat and reach New York.

Built to the design principles of Henry F. Swan, the *Beacon Light* was launched into the Tyne on March 2, 1890. The ceremony was performed by Mrs Stewart, of Liverpool. The vessel had been built for Messrs. R. Stewart & Co., then one of the largest importers of petroleum in Liverpool.

The British oil tanker Silverlip. She was launched at Low Walker in November 1902. As well as carrying oil, she also burned oil as fuel for her engines and was a portent of the gradual decline in the use of coal at sea.

On her trials, which probably took place on the measured mile off St Mary's Island, the vessel attained a mean speed of 11 knots. There were no problems reported. She returned to the Tyne for bunker coal before proceeding to sea on her first voyage.

The ship duly left for New York. On May 13 the *Beacon Light* encountered a mist which prevented her lookout men from seeing any great distance ahead. It was becoming colder but the captain did not suspect icebergs. Then the lookout on the forecastle shouted: 'Ice ahead!' A white mass towered over the tanker and shortly afterwards she struck a huge iceberg. The officer of the watch had ordered the engines stopped and then reversed, but the ship's headway was too great to prevent the impact.

Umbrella time. It was a dull and rainy day when this picture was taken of the crowds at the launch of the tanker Silverlip on November 29, 1902.

As the *Beacon Light* hit the berg a heavy pinnacle of ice, reportedly weighing 50 tons, fell off it on to the ship's bow, smashing in the steel deck. Some of the vessel's plates abaft the bow were also broken by the ice.

The ship was now holed in several places. Fortunately, these openings were largely plugged by ice and this may have helped to keep her afloat. Despite this, the sea poured into the forward compartment. The steam pumps were put into action and with difficulty the *Beacon Light* managed to limp into New York, albeit in a sinking condition. By this time she had more than 2,500 tons of water aboard. She was immediately put into dry dock. There does not appear to have been any injury or loss of life.

After this dramatic voyage, the tanker lasted for nearly 28

years. However, her luck ran out in February 1918 when she was torpedoed and sunk by a U-boat 15 miles south-east of the Butt of Lewis. She had been steaming from Liverpool to Scapa Flow naval base with fuel oil. Thirty-two men, including the captain, were killed.

On November 29, 1902, the oil tanker *Silverlip* was launched at Low Walker. It was evidently a grand occasion, for the chief guest was the Lord Mayor of London, Sir Marcus Samuel, chairman of the Shell Transport and Trading Co.

The previous day the Lord Mayor, the Lady Mayoress, and the Sheriffs of London and their ladies had taken a journey down the river in the steamer *J.C. Stephenson* at the invitation of the River Tyne Commissioners. In the evening they were guests of the Mayor and Corporation of Newcastle at the city's Grand Assembly Rooms.

It was reported that not only would the vessel carry petroleum, but petroleum would also be used for propelling her. Reporting the launch of the *Silverlip*, the *North Mail* told readers: 'It was a dull, rainy day. The coaly Tyne was in its darkest mood and seemed to frown at the steamer that was the embodiment of the discovery of a fuel that would supplement the coal which made it so great a waterway.'

Special trains took many prominent Newcastle people to Walker. Many of their faces were hidden under umbrellas as they crowded around the bows of the ship.

Naming the vessel, the Lady Mayoress dashed a bottle of wine against the ship's bow. A workman then rapidly pulled the bottle upwards in an attempt to save some of the wine, and another man was cheered by the crowd when he managed to catch several drops of the liquid in his cap.

Sadly, the *Silverlip* went on to have a relatively short career. On May 1, 1907, she was abandoned on fire in the Bay of Biscay after an explosion in one of her cargo tanks. She had been carrying benzine. Five men lost their lives.

The launch party for the British oil tanker Beme in 1904. A small girl has a day out to remember as she looks towards the camera at the head of the steps leading to the platform. The Beme had a long career, but was eventually sunk by the Italian submarine Refado Tarantini in the Mediterranean in 1940.

Far East Cruisers

Although the Low Walker Yard was mainly renowned for its merchant vessels, its order books also featured a considerable number of warships. Russia was the first foreign navy to do business with Mitchell's when two naval tenders, the *Ijora* and *Slavianka*, were launched in 1861. As we have seen, the *Staunch*, the first of a series of gunboats for various nations, was delivered in 1868.

Soon, however, the yard was building much larger warships. On June 6, 1883, the cruiser *Esmeralda* was launched at Low Walker. Built for Chile, she had been designed, like the *Staunch*, by Armstrong's partner George Rendel and was the first of the famous group of fast, hard-hitting protected warships which became known universally as 'Elswick Cruisers', even if a few of them were built at Low Walker. The *Esmeralda* had a speed in excess of 18 knots.

Sailors man the yards of the Chilean cruiser Esmeralda as she lies anchored in the Tyne following her completion in 1884 at Low Walker. The ship is saluting the Prince and Princess of Wales on the occasion of their visit to the Tyne to open the Coble Dene Dock (later the Albert Edward Dock) at North Shields. The royal couple are on the paddle steamer on the right, the Para E-Amazonas, built by Andrew Leslie & Co. of Hebburn for service on the River Amazon.

Earlier, in 1880, three other cruisers built to less satisfactory designs had been launched at Low Walker, two of which were ordered by China. These ships, the *Chao Yung* and *Yang Wei*, were lost at the Battle of the Yalu, fought between the Chinese and Japanese in 1894.

Gunfire from the Japanese ships set the *Chao Yung* on fire and she turned over and sank. Salvoes also set the *Yang Wei* ablaze and she ran aground. Wood in their superstructures and ornamentation had burned fiercely.

Low Walker and Elswick ships featured on both sides in this battle, which meant that Tyne-built vessels were fighting each other. They included Low Walker's cruiser *Naniwa* (sometimes referred to as the *Naniwa Kan*) which had been launched for the Japanese.

The *Naniwa* slid down the ways on March 18, 1885. Lady Armstrong performed the launch ceremony, dashing a bottle of wine against the ship's bow in the usual way. Japanese construction and engineering staff had supervised the progress of the work.

Following the launch, a dinner was held at the County Hotel, Newcastle, at which Sir William Armstrong presided. In a speech, he told guests, who included Prince Yamashino of Japan, that 'the ship that had been launched was for the service of a country which is never likely to come into collision with our own peace-loving country'.

The *Naniwa* was completed in early 1886 and was moved down river to Jarrow Slake as preparations began for her delivery voyage. A Japanese crew had arrived on Tyneside to man her. But just as things seemed to be going well, tragedy intervened. Takezo Fukamachi, an officer who bore the rank of paymaster, had a serious fall while aboard the vessel and died

A stern view of the Chinese cruiser Chao Yung on the stocks at Low Walker in 1880. She was sunk by Japanese warships at the Battle of the Yalu in 1894.

the next day from his injuries. He had fallen down the vessel's hold. The inquest, held aboard the *Naniwa*, recorded a verdict of 'accidental death'.

The paymaster is buried in Elswick Cemetery, his grave marked by an impressive obelisk. It bears an inscription in both English and Japanese, which reads: 'In memory of Jushichii Takezo Fukamachi, Imperial Japanese Navy, who was born on 18th August 1856, 4th Year of Ansei, and departed this life on the 19th February 1886.'

The cruiser *Naniwa* left the Tyne for her voyage to Japan in late March 1886. As well as the Battle of the Yalu, she also took part in the great naval clash between Russia and Japan at Tsushima in 1905. As mentioned previously, the victorious Japanese fleet at this battle was commanded by Admiral Togo.

In earlier years Togo had been captain of the *Naniwa*. The cruiser had intercepted a British merchant ship, the *Kow Shing*, carrying 1,500 Chinese troops to Korea on the outbreak of war between China and Japan in 1894. Controversially, the *Naniwa* sank the troopship after the Chinese refused to allow the British captain to surrender the vessel to Togo and accompany the *Naniwa* into port.

Two other Japanese cruisers, the *Takachiho* (or *Takachiho Kan*), a sister of the *Naniwa*, and *Takasago* were built at Low Walker. The *Takasago* was lost when she struck a mine near Port Arthur in 1904. The *Takachiho* was sunk by enemy action in October 1914 off Tsingtau, China, with the loss of over 240 men.

Low Walker also built ships for customers much closer to home than Japan. In 1897 two Norwegian coastal defence battleships slid down the ways, the *Harald Haarfagre* and the *Tordenskjold*.

The obelisk memorial to Takezo Fukamachi, paymaster of the Naniwa, in St John's Cemetery, Elswick, Newcastle.

The *Tordenskjold* was launched on March 18 of that year by Madame Nansen, wife of famed Arctic explorer Fridtjof Nansen. The ship had a long and useful career, but during the Second World War was captured by the Germans who equipped her with anti-aircraft guns. She was run aground before she could be handed back to the Norwegians after the end of the war in 1945.

The *Harald Haarfagre* was also seized by the Germans and she too served them for a while as an anti-aircraft guns ship. The vessel survived the war, but went to the breaker's yard in 1947.

The Japanese cruiser Naniwa (sometimes given her full name of Naniwa Kan). Launched at the Low Walker yard in 1885, she fought the Chinese at the Battle of the Yalu in 1894 and the Russians at Tsushima in 1905.

In 1898 a cruiser was launched 'on spec' at the yard in the knowledge that she was likely to find a buyer at a time when many fleets throughout the world were increasing their strength. The ship was named the *Fourth of July*, in honour of American Independence Day and fittingly she entered the Tyne on July 4.

However, things did not go entirely to plan. Miss Watts (probably the daughter of the ship's designer, Philip Watts) was to perform the ceremony but after several attempts failed to break the bottle of wine against the vessel's bows, the ship moved swiftly into the river. The bottle was left intact, although the spectators and workmen still cheered as the cruiser slid into the Tyne.

But it was unthinkable that the ship should not have it traditional baptism and Miss Watts and officials boarded a steam launch, catching up with the newly water-borne vessel. The naming ceremony was duly performed on the river.

Despite this slight hitch, which may have worried superstitious seamen, the *Fourth of July* was successful in finding a buyer and had a long career. She was sold to the Chilean Navy and renamed *Chacabuco*. The vessel was not broken up until the early 1950s.

Among the other Low Walker vessels which had a long life was the self-propelled hopper barge *Drudge*, launched on June 8, 1887, which was built to remove waste from Elswick. She had another use – guns of 110 tons or more could be mounted in the vessel and taken out to sea for testing.

The Norwegian coast defence battleship Harald Haarfagre surrounded by guests and spectators before her launch in 1897. A sister ship, the Tordenskjold, was launched in the same year.

The humble *Drudge* made a surge up the social scale in February 1901 when she became a Royal Navy trials gunboat following acquisition by the Admiralty. Her naval career was to last for 19 years. For a couple of these years she bore the unlikely name *Excellent*. The *Drudge* eventually ended up in a French shipbreaker's yard after a remarkable life spanning 82 years. She was still using her original engines, built by the Wallsend Slipway and Engineering Company, until the very end.

Runaway ship. The launch party for the cruiser Fourth of July, which entered the Tyne appropriately on 4 July 1898. The ship moved down the ways into the Tyne before the lady who was to have launched her was able to break the traditional bottle of wine over the vessel's bows. The ship was sold to Chile and renamed the Chacabuco, surviving until the early 1950s.

Low Walker's Last Ship

On December 31 1927 the firm of Armstrong Whitworth amalgamated some of its most important businesses with concerns owned by Vickers Ltd., of Barrow-in-Furness, to form Vickers-Armstrongs Ltd. The Low Walker Yard, the Walker Naval Yard and the Elswick Works, all in Newcastle, came under the ownership of the new company.

However, Low Walker was leased back by Vickers-Armstrongs to Sir W.G. Armstrong Whitworth & Co. Ltd., which still survived as a separate company. In 1929 this firm restructured its business so that a subsidiary company, Sir W.G. Armstrong Whitworth & Co. (Shipbuilders) Ltd., took control of Low Walker and of the old Dobson Yard at Walker and the former Tyne Iron Shipbuilding Yard at Willington Quay.

It was not long, however, before these yards were experiencing the effects of the great Depression of the early 1930s.

On December 19, 1930, the tanker *Elise* was launched into the Tyne from a Low Walker slipway for Norwegian owners. But the company's managing director, James Stewart, told guests: 'We have launched today one of the highly specialised inventions of man's ingenuity, an up to date tanker. Unfortunately, it leaves our shipbuilding berths at Walker absolutely empty, though we have one or two building in other yards.'

The position did not improve to any great degree. In 1934 the Low Walker Yard closed. Sir W.G. Armstrong Whitworth & Co. (Shipbuilders) Ltd. sold the yard to National Shipbuilders Security Ltd. Low Walker had simply run out of orders and in the final year or two only a small number of men were employed.

National Shipbuilders Security Ltd. had been formed to purchase redundant or obsolete shipyards, dismantle them and dispose of their contents, thus closing them down. It seemed the yard's life was at an end.

But the outbreak of the Second World War brought renewed demand for ships. Low Walker's slipways reopened in 1942 under the Tyne Branch of the Shipbuilding Corporation Ltd. The yard was placed under the management of Armstrong Whitworth. A series of cargo vessels were constructed for the war effort and many older workers returned to contribute their skills and experience.

With the arrival of peace in 1945 Low Walker continued to operate. The work included the completion of several ships which had been ordered during the war and a series of self-propelled barges for the Irawaddy Flotilla Company.

The final ship from the Low Walker Yard was the cargo carrier *Zarian*, which had originally been ordered by the Ministry of War Transport with the intention of naming her *Empire Birdsay*. However, she was launched as the *Zarian* for the United Africa Company on August 16, 1947. Later the ship was sold to the Palm Line and renamed *Lokoja Palm*. Speaking at the launch ceremony, Edwin Graham, general manager, praised the readiness with which older workers had returned to Low Walker to help meet the vital needs of wartime.

The yard closed in 1948 after a proud history during which management and workers had made a major contribution towards establishing the Tyne as one of the world's most important shipbuilding rivers. Similarly, the Elswick Yard had contributed in great measure to that global renown. Charles Mitchell's partnership with William Armstrong had proved a triumph.

John Clarkson, Longston

The final ship. The Lokoja Palm was launched on 16 August 1947 under the name Zarian. The vessel was broken up in China in 1971.

Select index of ships